CW00661338

DAVID GOWER'S
CRICKET
QUIZ BOOK

DAVID GOWER'S
CRICKET
QUIZ BOOK

DAVID GOWER
WITH PATRICK ALLEN

CollinsWillow
An Imprint of HarperCollinsPublishers

All rights reserved

First published in 1994 by
CollinsWillow
an imprint of HarperCollins *Publishers*
London

© David Gower Promotions Ltd 1994

A CIP catalogue record for this book
is available from the British Library

ISBN 0 00 218482 6

Printed and bound in Great Britain by
HarperCollins Manufacturing, Glasgow

Contents

Introduction

BY DAVID GOWER

Having never been overconcerned myself with statistics and averages, I have been amazed by the general love of records and the interest shown in them by the cricketing public since I swapped bat for pen and microphone.

Cricket, as a game steeped in history, has a literature unequalled in any other sport in terms of volume and variety, and the number of statisticians seems to grow by the season. Moreover, one-day cricket has opened yet another another dimension for the cricket lover and fanatic even if, as a player, it was not my favourite version of the game.

It is my earnest hope that this quiz book, which covers the highways and byways of cricket by means of more than 1,000 questions, keeps you guessing and allows you to score without too many flashes outside off-stump.

Each quiz is divided into three parts:

Quick single – easy runs to be had to keep the scoreboard ticking over.
Half century – more difficult, may demand patience (not one of my strongest suits!)
Century – very difficult; concentration and determination needed here to build an innings.

The cricket trivia chapter has been designed to give everyone a chance even with the most difficult questions. And to wrap things up, the answers are to be found at the back of the book.

Have fun and enjoy the challenge!

CHAPTER 1

England
Test Cricket

Debuts

*'Although hitting my first ball in Test cricket for four
would have to rank as a reasonable way to launch a
career, the Pakistani attack at the time (the 1978
summer) could hardly be equated to the West Indies sides
of the eighties and nineties.'*

Quick single

1. Which current England cricketer made a pair on his first Test
    match appearance v Australia in 1975?

2. Who was the Surrey batsman who made a century on his Test
    Match debut v Australia in 1993.

3. Which four players made their England debuts in the match
    v Australia at Trent Bridge in 1993?

4. Which Sussex cricketer, now playing for Surrey, was called
    up to play for England v New Zealand at Christchurch in
    1983–84?

5. Which cricketer made his debut for England in the first Test
    match of the 1994 series v South Africa at Lord's?

6. Prior to Michael Atherton who was the last Lancashire
    player to captain England at Old Trafford?

7. Which Surrey player made his debut v South Africa at The
    Oval at the age of 33?

Half century

8. Who in 1993 became the first Australian for a hundred years
    to make his maiden first class century in a Test match?

9. Who scored a century on the occasion of the first Test match between Australia and England in 1876–77?

10. Which Australian batsman scored a century on his first appearance v England at The Oval in 1981?

11. Which player appeared for England in one Test match at Adelaide in 1986–87 and has not played since?

12. Where did Greg Chappell score his first Test century and against whom?

13. Which two Gloucestershire players made their debuts in the same match for England v Sri Lanka in 1988?

14. Which player, now aged 43, made his Test debut at the age of 37 against the West Indies?

Century

15. Who was dismissed first ball in his only Test innings?

16. Which batsman put on 283 for the first wicket for England v Australia at Sydney in 1965–66 with Geoffrey Boycott?

17. Who scored 169 not out v Australia at The Oval in the same test as Len Hutton scored his 364 in 1938?

18. Who scored 94 on his Test debut v Sri Lanka at Lord's in 1988.

19. Which England player made his Test debut in Sri Lanka's inaugural Test match in Colombo in 1982?

20. Name the only England player, now a first-class umpire, to score a hundred at Lord's on his debut in Tests.

21. Which former Secretary of MCC, who died in 1993, scored his maiden first-class century on his debut for England in a Test match?

See Answers page 123

Partnerships

*'In 1985 I was involved in two large
partnerships with Tim Robinson at Edgbaston and
Graham Gooch at The Oval – so my concentration
couldn't have been too bad!'*

Quick single

22. Who was Allan Border's partner in the unbroken fifth wicket stand of 332 v England at Headingley in 1993?

23. Which two brothers each scored hundreds in the same innings of a Test match at The Oval in 1972?

24. Which two England batsmen hold the fourth wicket record partnership in Test cricket of 411?

25. Who was Geoff Boycott's first opening partner in Test cricket?

26. Which three opening batsmen did England use in the Test series v New Zealand and South Africa in 1994?

27. Which England batsman has participated in the greatest number of opening partnerships of more than 100 v Australia?

28. What is the record tenth wicket partnership for England v Australia?

Half century

29. When and where was the only occasion that David Gower and Graham Gooch shared a partnership of over 300 v Australia?

30. What is the record opening partnership by either side in Test matches between England and Australia?

31. What was the record opening partnership in Ashes Tests until broken by Geoff Marsh and Mark Taylor in 1989?

32. Which two batsmen were involved in a last wicket partnership at The Oval in 1902 v Australia when the famous quote 'We'll get them in singles' is alleged to have been made – England winning the match by one wicket?

33. Where did Australia make 301 without loss on the first day of a Test match?

34. Which cricketer put on 117 for the eighth wicket with Ian Botham at Headingley in 1981, scoring 56?

35. Which two cousins shared an unbroken sixth wicket partnership of 274 for West Indies v England at Lord's in 1966?

Century

36. Which two batsmen both scored 234 and were involved in a Test record partnership of 405 for the fifth wicket?

37. Which two English batsmen put on 215 for the sixth wicket at Trent Bridge in 1977, equalling the record for Ashes Tests?

38. What is the highest partnership for England against New Zealand?

39. What was the highest opening partnership between Len Hutton and Cyril Washbrook for England in Test cricket?

40. In which Test match were both the eighth and tenth wicket partnership by England v West Indies bettered?

41. Which England opening partners shared 11 first-wicket, three-figure partnerships against Australia?

42. Which two England opening batsmen twice made three-figure stands in each innings of a Test match v Australia?

See Answers page 124

14

Batsmen

'If I had more of Geoff Boycott's application and dedication to the game, I might have scored a lot more Test runs, but would not have made nearly as many friends.'

Quick single

43. What was David Gower's highest score in Test cricket?

44. What is the highest score by a right-handed batsman in Test cricket?

45. In which 1993 Test match were there two scores of 99 and who made them?

46. Which England batsmen, other than David Gower, made centuries v Australia at Edgbaston in 1985?

47. Who was the last cricketer to be given out handled the ball in a first-class match in England?

48. Who scored 240 for England v Australia at Lord's in 1938?

49. Who topped the Australian batting averages in the 1993 Test series v England?

Half century

50. Who scored a century for England in the Centenary Test between Australia and England in Melbourne in 1977?

51. Which England player in his first Test match against Australia in 1985 scored 175 at Headingley?

52. In the third Test of the 1985 England v Australia series, in which David Gower scored 166, which two Australian batsmen also scored centuries?

53. Which two batsmen in the 1964 Test match between England and Australia at Old Trafford made 311 and 256 respectively?

54. Who scored 95 as nightwatchman for England v Australia at Sydney in 1982–83?

55. Where and when did David Gower score his first Test century against Australia?

56. Which England batsman scored three Test match centuries on the 1986–87 tour of Australia?

Century

57. Who are the four England batsmen to score more than 700 runs in a Test series v Australia?

58. Name the only four batsmen to score more than 3000 runs in England v Australia Tests.

59. Name the only Australians to score more than 800 runs in a Test series against England.

60. What is the greatest number of runs scored before dismissal in Ashes Tests?

61. In which year did Jack Hobbs score his only Test hundred against Australia at The Oval?

62. Who was the first Australian to make a Test match century at Lord's?

63. Which English cricketer in the 1975 series v Australia averaged over 60 with the bat and took a wicket in his first over?

See Answers page 125

Bowlers

'In all my Test innings I was always keen to get the first headhunter out of the way early, as there is always the satisfaction in finding everything in working order early on.'

Quick single

64. Which leg-spinner has taken the greatest number of wickets in an Ashes series?

65. Which bowler dismissed Don Bradman for a duck second ball in his last Test match innings at The Oval in 1948?

66. Which bowler at Edgbaston in 1985 took 10–104 v. Australia?

67. Who took 16 wickets in a Test match v England at Lord's in 1972?

68. Which Australian bowler took 42 wickets in a series v England in 1981?

69. Who, with his first delivery in Test cricket in England, dismissed Mike Gatting?

70. In which Test match did Phil Tufnell first take five wickets in an innings for England?

Half century

71. Which Australian bowler in the fourth Test at Old Trafford v England in 1985 took 8–141?

72. Which Australian fast bowler burst on to the scene in the 1978–79 series against England and took 41 wickets?

73. Which Australian bowler took 34 wickets in the series v England in 1982–83?

74. Name the bowler who has taken the greatest number of wickets in England v Australia Tests.

75. Who took 15–104 (7–61 and 8–43) for England v Australia at Lord's in 1934?

76. Who in the 1981 Headingley Test took 8–43 to bowl out Australia 19 runs short of victory?

77. Who, on his Test debut v Australia at Trent Bridge, Nottingham, in 1989, took 1–166.

Century

78. Who was the first bowler to take more than 40 wickets in a Test series twice?

79. Which Australian bowled 51 consecutive overs in the England v Australia Test match at Old Trafford in 1964?

80. Which bowler has conceded the most runs in a Test match innings?

81. Which Australian bowler recorded his best bowling figures in Tests v England in Brisbane in 1990–91?

82. Who took 7–40 in the fourth Test of the 1970–71 series at Sydney?

83. Which bowlers have taken five wickets in an innings for Australia v England on the most occasions?

84. Which Australian bowler in 19 Tests against England took 102 wickets and, in a total of 27 Tests, took 144 wickets at 22.59?

See Answers page 126

Wicketkeeping and Fielding

*'Fielding in the covers has always come naturally to me.
It also involves less scampering about on the boundary,
of course.'*

Quick single

85. Who did not concede a bye in Australia's innings of 632–4
    v England at Lord's in 1993.

86. Who was the first England wicketkeeper to take six catches in
    an innings v Australia in Test cricket?

87. Which two England wicketkeepers have received the greatest
    number of Test caps?

88. Who is the only England wicketkeeper to have exceeded 100
    dismissals in Ashes Test matches?

89. Which wicketkeeper took 40 catches off the same bowler in
    England v Australia Tests and who was the bowler?

90. Which player has taken the greatest number of catches in Test
    cricket?

91. Which England wicketkeeper has made the greatest number
    of dismissals in a Test series?

Half century

92. Who was the England wicketkeeper who made a century for .
    England v Australia at Old Trafford in 1989?

93. Which Australian has taken the greatest number of catches in
    an innings by a wicketkeeper in England v Australia Tests?

94. What is the record number of dismissals by a wicketkeeper in a Test series in England?

95. Which England wicketkeeper scored a century in the 1986–87 Test match in Perth?

96. Who held the slip catch to give England victory by 3 runs in the 1982–83 Test match v Australia at Melbourne?

97. Which fielder has taken the greatest number of catches in a series?

98. What is the greatest number of victims by a wicketkeeper in a Test series?

Century

99. Who was the reserve wicketkeeper to Bob Taylor on the 1978–79 England tour to Australia?

100. Which was the first team in Test history to lose 19 wickets in a match to catches?

101. Which England player kept wicket and also bowled slow leg-breaks in four Tests in the 1897–98 series?

102. Which England wicketkeeper has taken the greatest number of catches in a Test match?

103. Which fielder suffered a dislocated shoulder when trying to arrest a spectator during the Australia v England series in 1982–83?

104. Who was the wicketkeeper who made 18 dismissals in successive Test matches?

105. On what occasion did England use four wicketkeepers in a Test match and who were they?

See Answers page 127

Captains

'I enjoyed playing with Graham Gooch until the 1990–91 tour of Australia; he has been a good mate and I am full of admiration for what he has achieved...'

Quick single

106. Who was the Australian captain when England won back the Ashes in 1953?

107. Which England captain had the most matches without defeat v Australia?

108. When did David Gower become captain of England for the first time?

109. Which four players captained England v West Indies in 1988?

110. Who was the last captain to lead a South African side in England, prior to Kepler Wessels?

111. Who was the Australian captain to win all five Tests in a series v England in 1920–21?

112. Who is the oldest player to have captained England in a Test match against Australia?

Half century

113. Who is the youngest England captain in a home Test match against Australia?

114. What is the highest score by an England captain in a Test match in Australia?

115. Who captained England in the first match of the 1990–91 series against Australia?

116. Which England player has scored the greatest number of Test runs whilst captain?

117. Who captained New Zealand to their first Test victory over England in 1977–78?

118. Which captain of England was captain against Australia the greatest number of times?

119. Who in 1984 became the first England captain since 1948 to declare and lose?

Century

120. Who is the only specialist wicketkeeper to captain Australia this century?

121. Who has scored the slowest century in England v Australia Test matches?

122. Which Australian captain scored the slowest-ever double-century in Ashes history?

123. Name the three Australian captains to score a Test double-century in England.

124. Who are the only two England captains to score centuries in their first Test as captain?

125 Who were the England and Australian captains in the 1980 Lord's Centenary Test?

126. Who was the England captain when England lost their first Test match to New Zealand in 1977–78?

See Answers page 128

CHAPTER 2

Test Cricket Around The World

Australia

'There is no greater challenge in cricket than the fight for the Ashes. I was lucky enough to make five tours to Australia and played some of my best cricket there.'

Quick single

1. Which cricketer has succeeded Allan Border as captain of Australia?

2. Which cricketer preceded Allan Border as captain of Australia?

3. Which wicketkeeper has made the greatest number of dismissals in Test cricket?

4. Which Australian Test player was nicknamed 'The Unbowlable'?

5. Name the cricketer who has scored 27 Test centuries.

6. Which Australian has made the greatest number of Test centuries against the West Indies?

7. Who scored a century in Australia's inaugural Test match against Sri Lanka and was made Man of the Match?

Half century

8. Who was Man of the Series in both the home and away series between South Africa and Australia in 1993–94?

9. Which bowler took the most recent hat-trick in a Test match?

10. Name the Australian batsman who scored eight Test match centuries against South Africa.

11. Which slow left-arm bowler took 11–96 for Australia v West Indies at Sydney in 1988–89?

12. Which Australian scored two 'pairs' in successive Test matches in 1992–93?

13. What is the fastest hundred ever made in Test cricket?

14. Which player took 11–222 in the tied Test between Australia and West Indies at Brisbane in 1960–61?

Century

15. Which Australian took a Test match hat-trick against South Africa in 1957–58?

16. Who are the only two cricketers in England v Australia Tests to score centuries in each of their first two Tests?

17. Who made a hundred at Adelaide on his Test debut, aged 19?

18. Name the two Australians to have scored a century before lunch in a Test match.

19. Which Australian bowler performed the hat-trick in each South African innings at Manchester in the 1912 Triangular Tournament?

20. Who was the last Australian batsman to be run out in *both* innings of a Test match?

21. Who was the first cricketer to be run out backing up in a Test match?

See Answers page 129

West Indies

'Helmets are standard items of kit these days, especially in the West Indies, though some players resisted at first. From my era, Viv Richards and Richie Richardson are the only two who come to mind at the highest level.'

Quick single

22. Which first-class cricketer has the initials 'C E L' and what do they stand for?

23. Who has made the greatest number of Test centuries for the West Indies against Australia?

24. Who scored 619 runs at an average of 88.43 in West Indies Test series v India in 1988–89?

25. Which West Indian cricketer, who played 66 tests for West Indies, incurred a life ban from West Indian cricket for playing cricket in South Africa in 1982–83?

26. Which team was dismissed by the West Indies for 97 at Kingston, Jamaica in 1975–76 with five men absent hurt?

27. Which batsman has scored the greatest number of Test match centuries v West Indies?

28. Who captained West Indies in the greatest number of Test matches?

Half century

29. Which West Indies Test bowler has taken the greatest number of Test wickets?

30. In the Australia v West Indies series in 1988–89, which West Indies bowler took a hat-trick in a Test match?

31. Who scored 7,558 runs in 108 Tests, including 107 against India, on his maiden Test appearance at Bangalore in 1974–75?

32 Who in 1976 scored 1,710 Test runs in a calendar year.

33. What is the highest score by a West Indian in Australia in a Test match?

34. Which West Indian all-rounder was killed in a car crash in 1959, having played 26 Test matches, scored 1331 runs, and taken 48 wickets?

35. Which West Indian opening batsman and captain was shot and subsequently died from his wounds in 1989?

Century

36. Who jointly holds the West Indian first-wicket partnership records against all Test opponents except South Africa and Zimbabwe?

37. Which fielder threw down the wicket to achieve Test cricket's first tie at Brisbane in 1960?

38. Which West Indies fast bowler was hanged for the murder of his wife?

39. Who was the only West Indies Test captain born outside the West Indies?

40. Who is the only West Indian to take nine wickets in a Test innings?

41. Who, apart from Graham Gooch in 1990, is the only other batsman to score a century in each innings of a Test match at Lord's?

42. Which two West Indies batsmen scored hundreds in their first two innings in Test cricket?

Pakistan

'There really should have been no surprise about Shakoor Rana and the dust-up with Mike Gatting, since Mike had twice been given out lbw by Shakoor on his England debut in Karachi in 1978.'

Quick single

43. Who is the only Pakistani bowler to have taken over 300 Test wickets?

44. Which player, who subsequently played county cricket for Hampshire, became the second youngest Test player for Pakistan v New Zealand at Wellington in 1988–89 aged 16 years and 189 days.

45. Which former Surrey, Worcestershire and Glamorgan batsman waited over 17 years between Test caps?

46. Who is the only Pakistani to take 40 wickets in a Test series?

47. Who is the only Pakistani batsman to score a double-century at Lord's in a Test match?

48. Who is the current captain of Pakistan?

49. Who is the only Pakistan player to make a century and take 10 wickets in a Test match?

Half century

50. Name the four brothers who have all played Test cricket for Pakistan.

51. Who was the second batsman, after Geoffrey Boycott, to score his 100th century in a Test match?

52. Who has played the longest innings in first-class cricket?

53. Which Pakistani bowler took four wickets in five balls v West Indies at Lahore in 1990–91?

54. When did Waqar Younis and Wasim Akram first play together in a Test match for Pakistan?

55. What are the best bowling figures of Waqar Younis in Test cricket?

56. Who is the youngest batsman ever to have made a Test century?

Century

57. Who is the only Pakistani to be given out 'handled the ball' in a Test match?

58. Who was the first player to score a hundred in both his first and his 100th Test match?

59. Who are the only father and son both to have made Test double-centuries?

60. Which bowler has conceded the greatest number of runs in a Test innings without taking a wicket?

61. Which two Pakistani players hold the Test ninth wicket partnership and where was it achieved?

62. Who is the only Pakistani bowler to take ten wickets in an innings four times v England in Test matches?

63. In which match were the fewest number of runs scored in a full day's play in a Test match involving Pakistan?

See Answers page 131

India

*'The India tour of 1984–85 was a very happy one –
drug-free, scandal-free and we also won the Test series,
no mean achievement over there.'*

Quick single

64. Name the father and son who have both captained India on tours to England.

65. Who is the youngest-ever Test match captain?

66. Which player, after seven Test matches in 1992–93 in which he scored four centuries, had an average of 113.29?

67. Which bowler has delivered the greatest number of balls in Test cricket?

68. Who is the youngest player to score a half-century in Test cricket?

69. Whose Test match career ended after 4,378 runs at 42.50 in 69 Tests after calling the selectors 'a bunch of jokers'?

70. Which Indian batsman has scored the greatest number of centuries against England in Test cricket?

Half century

71. Who was Kapil Dev's 432nd victim in Test cricket to break the existing record of Richard Hadlee?

72. Which batsman has been most frequently dismissed by the first ball of a Test match?

73. Which Indian batsman scored two double-centuries in Test cricket in 1993?

74. Which batsman made the highest number of runs in his first Test series?

75. What is the highest fourth innings total to win a Test match?

76. Which Indian leg-spinner took 16–136 (8–61 and 8–75) on his Test match debut v West Indies at Madras in 1987–88?

77. Who has scored the greatest number of Test centuries?

Century

78. Who was Kapil Dev's first victim in Test cricket, and when?

79. Which Indian Test cricketer scored over 2,000 runs in Test cricket without scoring a century?

80. What is the highest individual score for India v Pakistan in Test matches?

81. Who captained India on their first Test tour of England in 1932?

82. Who was the last man dismissed in the tied Test between India and Australia at Madras in 1987–88?

83. Who was the first Indian to carry his bat through a completed Test innings?

84. Who is the only wicketkeeper to make five stumpings in an innings?

See Answers page 132

New Zealand

'New Zealand can be quite a testing tour, partially in trying to stay awake, and also because of the amount of travelling.'

Quick single

85. Who was captain of the 1994 New Zealand tourists to England?

86. Who captained New Zealand in their first-ever Test match in 1929–30?

87. Who was Richard Hadlee's 400th dismissal in Test cricket?

88. Which bowler, who returned figures of 7–52 for New Zealand v Pakistan in Faisalabad in 1990–91, admitted deliberately tampering with the ball?

89. Who has taken five wickets in an innings on the greatest number of occasions in Test cricket?

90. Which New Zealand batsman has scored the greatest number of Test match centuries against England?

91. Which New Zealand batsman scored 299 in a Test match v Sri Lanka?

Half century

92. Who was the most experienced international cricketer in the world before making a Test appearance?

93. What is the Test and first-class third-wicket record partnership?

94. Which New Zealand left-hander, a contemporary of David Gower, became the first New Zealander to score 5,000 runs in Tests?

95. Which wicketkeeper scored 173 (the highest score by a No. 9 batsman in Test cricket) for New Zealand v India at Auckland in 1990–91?

96. Who was the first New Zealander to take 100 Test wickets?

97. Who is the only New Zealander to take nine wickets in a Test innings?

98. What are the best match figures by a New Zealand bowler in Test cricket?

Century

99. Which New Zealander took a hat-trick in his first Test match?

100. What is the highest score by a player carrying his bat through a Test innings?

101. The fourth Test match in Test history was completely washed out by the weather. Where was it due to be played?

102. Name the four sets of brothers to have played Test cricket for New Zealand and to have appeared together.

103. Who are the six father/son combinations to play Test cricket for New Zealand?

104. Who, other than Richard Hadlee, is the only New Zealander to do the Test 'double' of 1000 runs and 100 wickets?

105. Who are the five New Zealand players to have scored more than 3,000 runs in Test cricket?

See Answers page 133

South Africa

'I was never tempted to play cricket, unauthorized cricket that is, in South Africa.'

Quick single

106. Who captained South Africa in their last official Test series in 1969–70 prior to their return to Test cricket?

107. When and where was South Africa's first Test victory in England?

108. What is the record score by a South African batsman in Test cricket v Australia?

109. Who is the only South African to achieve the Test double of 1000 runs and 100 wickets?

110. Who had match figures of 12–139 when South Africa won its first Test match for 22 years v India at Port Elizabeth in 1992–93?

111. What is the highest aggregate of Test runs by a South African batsman in a career?

112. Which South African player was chosen as Man of the Series in the 1994 series v England?

Half century

113. Who was the first South African to take a hundred Test match wickets?

114. Who is the youngest South African to score a Test century?

115. Which South African making his Test debut was dismissed by the first ball of a Test match?

116. Who scored a century for South Africa in their first Test match against the West Indies?

117. Who became the first non-white man to appear in a Test match for South Africa?

118. Which South African wicketkeeper scored 606 runs in a Test series against Australia?

119. Which South African made a maiden test century at his 62nd attempt?

Century

120. Who is the only South African to take nine wickets in a Test innings?

121. Who was the first cricketer to carry his bat through a Test innings?

122. Which player representing Zimbabwe in their inaugural Test match v India had previously played Test cricket for South Africa?

123. Who is the only South African to score a century on his Test debut?

124. Who on the 1910–11 South African tour of Australia scored 732 runs and took 49 wickets?

125. Who made the last century for South Africa in Test cricket before their isolation in 1970?

126. Who was the first South African batsman to score 2,000 runs in Test cricket?

See Answers page 134

CHAPTER 3

County Cricket

Batting

'It was true in my early career that I batted for England and fielded for Leicestershire. It was often difficult to pump up the adrenalin on a cold, dark day at Derby or Northampton.'

Quick single

1. Against which county, and where, did David Gower score his last first-class century before retirement?

2. What was David Gower's highest score in first-class cricket?

3. Which English player has the highest career average for a batsman who has scored more than 10,000 runs?

4. Who are the only two current English players to have an average of more than 50 in first-class cricket?

5. Who, in 1990, became the youngest batsman to score 50 first-class hundreds?

6. Which player, and for which county, made a double-century in his first championship match of the 1994 season, having made only 224 runs in the whole of 1993?

7. Which batsman, in his first Championship match for his county in 1994, beat an 80-year-old record, and what was it?

Half century

8. Who is the youngest player to achieve a career aggregate of 10,000 runs?

9. Where did David Gower score his first first-class century?

10. Against whom did David Gower made his Leicestershire County Championship debut?

11. Which two batsmen scored ten or more centuries in 1990?

12. What is the highest individual score ever made at The Oval, and whose record was beaten?

13. Who is the youngest player to score 2,000 runs in an English season, and how old was he?

14. Who scored 34,386 runs in a career that lasted from 1928 to 1955 and never played a Test match for England?

Century

15. Which cricketer scored 1000 runs in 28 consecutive seasons between 1907 and 1938?

16. Which player has scored the greatest number of runs in a career for Hampshire, and the greatest number by one man for one club?

17. David Gower made 21 centuries for Leicestershire; who has scored the greatest number for the county?

18. Which batsman has scored the highest proportion of his side's runs?

19. Which cricketers who have scored 100 centuries have scored fewest double-centuries?

20. Which player scored 189 not out of 227 in 90 minutes v Sussex at Hove in 1911?

21. Prior to Brian Lara's 501 not out at Edgbaston v Durham in 1994, what was the previous highest score by a left-hander in first-class cricket?

See Answers page 135

Bowling

*'One of the unhappiest Danes I ever saw was
Derbyshire's Ole Mortensen when he had an lbw
appeal turned down.'*

Quick single

22. For which county, other than Gloucestershire and Durham, did David Graveney appear?

23. For which county did Richard Stemp play before joining Yorkshire?

24. Which bowler currently playing county cricket completed 1000 wickets in a career in 1993?

25. Which bowler took the greatest number of wickets in the 1993 season?

26. For which two county sides has Winston Benjamin, the West Indies fast bowler appeared in first-class cricket?

27. Which bowler has taken the greatest number of first-class wickets?

28. Who statistically has produced the best bowling figures in an innings in county cricket?

Half century

29. Who took 2,090 wickets in eight successive seasons, taking over 200 wickets in each of the seasons?

30. What is Graham Gooch's best bowling performance in first-class cricket?

31. Which current county cricketer took 5–105 on his first appearance for Western Australia v Victoria at Melbourne in 1990–91?

32. Which Derbyshire fast bowler only received two Test caps in 1949 and 1961, although he took 1,670 wickets for the county at 17.11?

33. Which Middlesex bowler took 100 wickets in a season in 1983?

34. Which player from Glamorgan took 2,218 wickets in his career and did not play a Test match for England?

35. Which Somerset player was fined £250 for ball tampering in a 2nd XI match v Nottinghamshire at Glastonbury?

Century

36. Which bowler, in 1990, took 14 wickets in 454.4 overs at an average of 103.36 per wicket?

37. Who, in 1990, went to the wicket 16 times for an aggregate of three runs at an average of 0.50?

38. When was the last occasion in England that eleven bowlers were used in an innings?

39. Who, prior to Richard Johnson's 10–45 v Derbyshire in 1994, was the last bowler to take all 10 wickets in an innings in the County Championship?

40. Which bowler took 100 wickets in a season for 20 successive years from 1949–1968?

41. Who in 1990 returned the best innings bowling analysis of the season in first-class cricket?

42. Who was no-balled for bowling under-arm without informing the striker of a change of action in 1990?

See Answers page 137

All-rounders

*'A player who could be classified as an all-rounder,
Shaun Udal has impressed me both for his spin bowling
and his application while batting.'*

Quick single

43. Which Lancashire player took 8–30 and scored 117 v Hampshire at Old Trafford in 1994?

44. Which England all-rounder suffered a detached retina in 1994 but subsequently played regular county cricket during the season?

45. Which West Indian all-rounder was Nottinghamshire's overseas player in 1994?

46. Which Kent player scored 58,969 runs in his career and took 2068 wickets?

47. Who was the only player to score 1000 runs and take more than 50 wickets in the 1993 season?

48. Which overseas all-rounder was replaced by Brian Lara as Warwickshire's overseas player for 1994?

49. Who was the bowler hit for six 6's in an over by Gary Sobers?

Half century

50. Who was Leicestershire's captain in their Championship winning year?

51. Which player scored 3,000 runs and took 100 wickets in season?

52. Which cricketer, who became eligible for England in 1994, has previously played 11 one-day internationals for Zimbabwe?

53. Which player achieved the greatest number of doubles (1000 runs and 100 wickets) in a season?

54. Which South African all-rounder captained Derbyshire and later acted as coach to Gloucestershire?

55. Who are the only two players to achieve the double since the reduction of County Championship matches in 1969?

56. Which Australian all-rounder who played 16 limited-over internationals for Australia played county cricket for Somerset in 1991–92?

Century

57. Who is the only player to score a hundred and take a hat-trick on two separate occasions?

58. Which two Essex all-rounders went to the same school and played for England 57 years apart?

59. Who was the last double cricket and soccer international to play for England?

60. Who in 1906 became the first player to score 2,000 runs and take 200 wickets in a first day season?

61. Who are the only two players to have scored a hundred in each innings and taken 10 wickets in a match?

62. Who are the only three Yorkshiremen to have scored over 20,000 runs or taken 2000 wickets in a career?

63. Who was the last player to be dismissed 'handled ball' in the County Championship?

See Answers page 138

Overseas Players

'I very much believe in overseas players in the county game, it prevents players becoming too insular.'

Quick single

64. Who was Durham's first overseas player on joining the County Championship?

65. Who was Yorkshire's first overseas player?

66. Which cricketer have Gloucestershire signed up to be their overseas player for 1995?

67. Who was Durham's overseas player for 1994?

68. For which English county did Greg Chappell, Martin Crowe, and Sunil Gavaskar play county cricket?

69. For which county did the West Indian fast bowler Michael Holding play first-class cricket?

70. Which four members of the West Indies Test team were in the Warwickshire championship side of 1972?

Half century

71. Name the player that Yorkshire have signed up as their overseas player for 1995.

72. Who, at the age of 35 in 1989, made his debut in county cricket and in the next three years compiled 7,604 runs at an average of 72.41, with 28 hundreds, before becoming a Test player?

73. Name the three West Indians with the surname 'Benjamin' to play county cricket in 1993.

74. Which West Indies batsman shares with Geoff Humpage the English fourth-wicket record stand of 470?

75. What was the highest score of Viv Richards' first-class career?

76. Which overseas player, in his first full season of English county cricket, scored 2,395 runs at 47.90 in 1968?

77. Which Australian, then aged 42, scored 3,000 runs and took 62 wickets for Somerset? (He later became a first-class umpire.)

Century

78. Who achieved the double for MCC in first-class matches on tour in 1926–27 to India and Ceylon?

79. Who is the only batsman to have hit the ball over the present Lord's pavilion?

80. What is the highest score by a South African player in the County Championship?

81. Who, in his first season of county cricket, reached 1,000 runs in only 12 innings?

82. Who is the only current batsman to have scored over 40,000 runs?

83. Who, in his only season in first-class cricket as an overseas player, took 85 wickets at 14.72 runs each in 1980?

84. For which English county did Ian Chappell and Geoff Lawson play?

See Answers page 139

Wicketkeepers and Fielders

'The bubbly personality of Steve Rhodes is of inestimable value to the current England side.'

Quick single

85. Which former Kent wicketkeepers now play for Middlesex and Surrey respectively?

86. Which former wicketkeeper who played for England in one-day internationals is now the Middlesex coach?

87. Which wicketkeeper dropped Brian Lara on 18 during his innings of 501 not out for Warwickshire v Durham at Edgbaston in 1994?

88. Which fielder took the greatest number of catches in both 1992 and 1993?

89. Which wicketkeeper has made the most consecutive County Championship appearances?

90. Who was the last wicketkeeper to be made Young Cricketer of the Year?

91. Who was the last full-time wicketkeeper to be one of Wisden's five Cricketers of the Year?

Half century

92. Who was the last wicketkeeper to take a hat-trick (three catches off successive balls)?

93. Which current county cricketer has taken over 500 catches in his career?

94. Who was the first Test match wicketkeeper to make 200 dismissals?

95. Who is the only wicketkeeper to have scored 2000 runs and made 100 dismissals in a season?

96. Which player has taken the greatest number of catches in his first-class career?

97. Which fielder has taken the greatest number of catches in a season?

98. Which player in 1991 scored a century and achieved eight dismissals in an innings?

Century

99. Which wicketkeeper has made the greatest number of dismissals in his career?

100. Who is the only wicketkeeper to make 100 dismissals three times in a season?

101. Who are the only two cricketers to take seven catches as a fielder in an innings?

102. Which English county wicketkeeper scored 1000 runs in first-class cricket in 1994 (the first since 1928 to do so for his county)?

103. Which is the only recorded instance in first-class cricket of a hat-trick in which all the victims were stumped?

104. Which player has taken the greatest number of catches as a fielder in a season since the reduction of the County Championship in 1969?

105. Who are the only players to achieve the wicketkeepers double of 1000 runs and 100 dismissals in a season?

See Answers page 140

General knowledge

*'Probably my closest friend at Leicester was
Brian Davison, a tremendous batsman and destroyer
of any bowling attack.'*

Quick single

106. Which former Gloucestershire cricketer is now the captain of Durham?

107. Which three international players left Somerset at the end of the 1986 season?

108. For which county did Jim Laker appear in first-class cricket after leaving Surrey?

109. Who did Courtney Walsh succeed as captain of Gloucestershire?

110. Who did Graham Gooch succeed as captain of Essex?

111. Which Yorkshire player was fined £500 for dissent by the TCCB in 1994?

112. When did Britannic Assurance begin their sponsorship of the County Championship?

Half century

113. Which Middlesex and England bowler had played 13 Test matches before receiving his county cap?

114. Which current Sussex cricketers have been capped by three counties?

115. Which two bowlers swapped counties before the 1994 season?

116. Which Manchester United footballer played one Test match for England in 1985 and took almost 600 first-class wickets for Yorkshire?

117. Who was the last player to score 2,000 runs and take 100 wickets in an English season?

118. When was the last first-class match to begin and finish on the same day?

119. Which first-class cricketer's benefit match was begun and finished on the same day?

Century

120. Who was the first English county cricketer to play for four separate counties and who were they?

121. When was the last tied match in English first-class cricket?

122. What is the highest match aggregate in a first-class match in Britain, which counties were involved, and how many wickets fell in the match?

123. Which is the only county to win a championship match without losing a wicket in either innings?

124. Who, in 1989, completed a pair on two different pitches?

125. Which players have made more than 700 appearances in the County Championship?

126. Which player made the most consecutive County Championship appearances?

See Answers page 141

CHAPTER 4

One-Day Cricket

Internationals

*'I was quite proud of my 158 against New Zealand in
Brisbane in 1982–83. It turned out to be my highest
score in limited-overs internationals.'*

Quick single

1. Which two players made their one-day international debuts
   for England v New Zealand at Edgbaston in May 1994?

2. What is the highest innings score in a one-day international?

3. What is the highest individual score by an Englishman in a
   one-day international?

4. Who in the final of the Sharjah Cup took a hat-trick and 7–37
   for Pakistan in the final v India in 1991–92, the best bowling
   figures in one-day internationals?

5. Which cricketer has so far appeared in the greatest number of
   one-day internationals?

6. Which wicketkeeper has made the greatest number of
   dismissals in limited-over internationals?

7. Who was the last player to make centuries in successive one-
   day internationals in England?

Half century

8. When was the first one-day international and which teams
   were involved?

9. Which bowler took a hat-trick v Sri Lanka in the final of the
   one-day Asia Cup in 1990–91 at Calcutta?

10. Which cricketer has made the highest individual score in a one-day international?

11. Which cricketer has scored the greatest number of runs in one-day internationals?

12. Who has taken the greatest number of wickets in one-day internationals?

13. What is the lowest innings total in a one-day international?

14. Who has scored the greatest number of centuries in one-day international cricket?

Century

15. Which current All Black rugby international has played cricket in one-day internationals for New Zealand?

16. Which Surrey player, who has not played Test cricket, appeared for England in three one-day internationals v West Indies in 1988?

17. What is the best analysis by an England bowler in a one-day international?

18. Which Australian has scored the greatest number of one day centuries?

19. Which player, selected for the one-day international series against Australia in 1993, failed to play a match in the three-game series?

20. How many English bowlers have taken more than 100 wickets in one-day internationals?

21. Which Yorkshire cricketer, who later played minor counties cricket for Lincolnshire, played one-day internationals for England in 1981?

See Answers page 142

NatWest Trophy/Gillette Cup

*'There are times when motivation becomes difficult,
particularly in one-day matches, but this certainly was
not a problem during the summer of 1991 when
Hampshire won the NatWest Trophy under my captaincy.'*

Quick single

22. Who was the Man of the Match in the 1993 NatWest Trophy final between Sussex and Warwickshire?

23. Who was Man of the Match in the NatWest final for two different counties?

24. Which year did David Gower captain Hampshire to victory in the NatWest Trophy final?

25. What is the highest individual score in the final of the Gillette Cup/NatWest Trophy since its inception in 1963?

26. What is the highest individual score in the NatWest Trophy?

27. Which player has won the greatest number of Man of the Match awards in the NatWest Trophy?

28. Who was the Man of the Match in the 1994 NatWest final at Lord's?

Half century

29. Who has scored the fastest hundred in the Gillette Cup/NatWest Trophy?

30. Who won the Gillette Cup three times in succession in 1970, 1971 and 1972?

31. Which bowler has taken the most wickets in the NatWest Trophy/Gillette Cup in a career?

32. Who captained Sussex to victory in the first two years of the Gillette Cup in 1963 and 1964?

33. In which year of the Gillette Cup/NatWest Trophy were centuries scored for both the winning and losing sides?

34. Name the first minor county to reach the quarter-finals of the Gillette Cup.

35. Who has scored the greatest number of centuries in the Gillette Cup/NatWest Trophy?

Century

36. What is the best-ever bowling performance in the NatWest Trophy?

37. Which was the first minor county to beat a first-class county in the Gillette Cup?

38. What is the highest wicket partnership in the Gillette Cup/NatWest Trophy?

39. Who has taken 4 wickets in 5 balls in the Gillette Cup? NatWest Trophy?

40. Who took 5–26 v Northamptonshire in the NatWest Trophy Final in 1990 to win the Man of the Match award?

41. Which player has scored the greatest number of runs in the NatWest/Gillette Cup during his career?

42. Who has scored the fastest hundred in a NatWest final?

See Answers page 144

Benson and Hedges Cup

'Leicestershire's defeat of Essex in the 1985 Benson and Hedges Cup final was a memorable moment in my career – and all the sweeter considering the standard of the opposition.'

Quick single

43. Which two counties contested the 1994 Benson and Hedges Cup Final?

44. Who won the 1993 Benson and Hedges Cup Final?

45. Who was Man of the Match in the 1994 Benson and Hedges Cup Final?

46. Name the three first-class counties that have never reached the final of the Benson and Hedges Cup?

47. Who won the Gold Award in the Benson and Hedges Final in 1984, although he made 0 and did not bat?

48. Who won their first one-day final at the seventh attempt in 1991 when beating Lancashire in the Benson and Hedges Cup?

49. Whose total of 352–6 would have been the highest score in the Benson and Hedges Cup in a match between first-class counties had it not been declared void due to weather interruption?

Half century

50. Who were the first winners of the Benson and Hedges Cup?

51. Which counties have won the Benson and Hedges Cup the greatest number of times?

52. Who lost a bowl out for a place in the semi-finals of the 1994 Benson & Hedges Cup, and to whom?

53. Who was Man of the Match in the 1993 Benson and Hedges Cup Final?

54. What is the lowest total ever in a Benson and Hedges match?

55. What is the highest score ever made in a Benson and Hedges Cup Final?

56. What is the highest wicket partnership in the Benson and Hedges Cup?

Century

57. Who, in 1982, became the only wicketkeeper to take eight catches in a one-day match?

58. Name the captain who declared his side's innings closed before facing a ball, to ensure qualification for the knockout stages of the Benson and Hedges Cup?

59. Who hit the last ball of the 1989 Benson and Hedges Cup Final for 4 to win the Cup for his side?

60. Who is the only bowler to take a hat-trick in a Benson & Hedges Cup Final?

61. Name the only two players to have scored centuries in the Benson and Hedges Cup Final.

62. Who are the only two players to take five wickets in an innings in a Benson and Hedges Cup Final?

63. What is the best bowling performance ever in the Benson & Hedges Cup?

See Answers page 145

Sunday League

'The decision to increase the number of overs per innings in the Sunday League from 40 overs to 50 meant it was an even harder slog for the players, as well as the spectators. Thankfully, that decision has been reversed.'

Quick single

64. Who scored the greatest number of runs in the AXA Equity and Law Sunday League in 1994?

65. Who won the AXA Equity and Law Sunday League in 1994?

66. What is the lowest total ever made in a Sunday League innings?

67. Which player has hit the greatest number of sixes in a Sunday League season?

68. What is the most expensive bowling analysis in the Sunday League?

69. Which county in winning their first ever limited over competition were Sunday League Champions in 1993?

70. What is the highest ever innings total in the Sunday League?

Half century

71. What is the best bowling performance ever recorded in the Sunday League?

72. What is the highest score in the Sunday League, and by whom?

73. Which was the first year in which coloured clothing was worn in AXA & Equity Sunday League?

74. Which player has scored the greatest number of centuries in the Sunday League?

75. Who has taken the greatest number of wickets in his career in the Sunday League?

76. Which team has won the greatest number of Sunday League matches?

77. Which player has scored the greatest number of runs in a season in the Sunday League?

Century

78. Which batsman has scored the greatest number of runs in their career in the Sunday League?

79. Which batsman has hit the greatest number of sixes in a season in the Sunday League?

80. What is the highest-ever wicket partnership in the Sunday League and who were the batsmen?

81. Who, in 1969, had an analysis 8–8–0–0 in the Sunday League?

82. Which bowlers have taken the greatest number of wickets in a season in the Sunday League?

83. Which wicketkeeper has made the most dismissals in his career in the Sunday League?

84. Which players have taken seven or more wickets in an innings in the Sunday League?

See Answers page 146

World Series

'The razzmatazz of World Series Cricket is here to stay.'

Quick single

85. What was the name of the tycoon responsible for World Series Cricket?

86. Who was the main recruiting agent for the WSC in England?

87. Who was the man of the series in the 1992–93 WSC Finals?

88. Who was the only South African century maker in the WSC finals of 1993–94?

89. Which player captained his side for the 100th time in WSC internationals in 1993–94?

90. What was David Gower's highest score in World Series Cricket?

91. Who was the first player to play in 200 one day internationals?

Half century

92, Which two players captained their countries for the 100th time in one-day international matches in the same match?

93. Who scored three centuries in the Benson and Hedges World Series Cricket Cup in 1982–83?

94. Who was the Man of the Finals in the 1989–90 WSC series?

95. In which year did England win the Benson and Hedges WSC Cup and who was the captain?

96. Which two players were joint Players of the Finals in the 1991–92 WSC Cup?

97. Which batsman scored the only century in the B&H WSC Cup in 1990–91?

98. Who was Man of the Finals in the 1990–91 Benson and Hedges WSC Cup?

Century

99. Which player was instructed by whom to bowl underarm and along the ground to prevent New Zealand winning a B & H WSC Finals match in 1980–81?

100. Who was the New Zealand batsman facing the underarm delivery?

101. Who in a WSC match at Sydney in 1989–90 received the Man of the Match award although the judges stated publicly it would have been given to Imran Khan had they not been under pressure from Channel Nine to name the winner before the match was over?

102. Which player who had been dismissed by his first ball in Test cricket was also dismissed by his first ball in a WSC one day international in 1993–94?

103. What is the record aggregate of runs in a WSC match?

104. Who had a bowling analysis of 10–8–3–4 in a one-day WSC international between West Indies and Pakistan in 1992–93?

105. What is the record opening stand in WSC matches?

See Answers page 147

World Cup

*'Under Imran Khan, Pakistan's World Cup team
of 1991–92 were transformed from consistent
underachievers to spirited competitors.'*

Quick single

106. Who won the World Cup in 1991–92?

107. Who won the World Cup Final in Calcutta in 1987?

108. Where is the 1995–96 World Cup to be held?

109. Which England batsman scored 115 in the World Cup semi-final v India at Bombay in 1987?

110. What is the best ever bowling in a World Cup match?

111. Who scored 138 not out off 156 balls in the 1979 Final at Lord's?

112. Which player scored the highest aggregate of runs in the 1983 World Cup?

Half century

113. What is the highest score ever made in the World Cup?

114. Who was Man of the Match when Australia beat England at Calcutta in 1987?

115. What is the most expensive bowling analysis in the World Cup?

116. What is the least expensive analysis in the World Cup?

117. Who, in the 1975 World Cup v England, batted through 60 overs for 36 not out?

118. Who won the Man of the Match in the World Cup semi-final between Pakistan and Australia at Lahore in 1987?

119. Who were the sponsors of the 1987 World Cup?

Century

120. Who was Man of the Match in the 1983 World Cup Final between India and West Indies at Lord's?

121. Who is the only player to score a century in a World Cup Final?

122. Which bowler, by taking 6–14, destroyed England's chances of reaching the 1975 World Cup Final at Headingley?

123. What is the highest partnership achieved in a World Cup match for the ninth wicket?

124. Which Australian bowler took five wickets in the 1975 final v West Indies at Lord's?

125. Who captained Zimbabwe in their first World Cup tournament in 1983?

126. In 1983 when India won the World Cup which of their players took the greatest number of wickets in the entire tournament?

See Answers page 148

CHAPTER 5

Cricket Grounds

England

'Certain moments stay with you quite vividly, and my first Test century at The Oval was certainly one of them.'

Quick single

1. Who was Man of the Match for England v Australia at The Oval in 1993?

2. Where was the first Test match in England played?

3. What is the highest score ever made at Lord's cricket ground?

4. What is the highest score ever made in a Test match at Trent Bridge, Nottingham?

5. Which two Yorkshiremen made their Test match debuts in the first Test v New Zealand at Trent Bridge, Nottingham, in 1994?

6. Who is the only player to take 10 wickets and score a half-century in a Test match at Lord's?

7. What is the highest score by a New Zealander in a Test match at Lord's?

Half century

8. In which year did England last beat Australia at Lord's in a Test match?

9. Where was an England v Australia Test match abandoned due to vandalism?

10. What was the name of Shane Warne's fellow spinner in the 1993 England v Australia Test series?

11. Who were the two batsmen who saved the 1953 Lord's Test match against Australia?

12. Who in the 1980 Centenary Test at Lord's between England and Australia scored 117 and 84?

13. Which England batsman in Botham's match at Old Trafford in 1981 scored 78 in seven hours?

14. Which cricketer, other than Graham Gooch, has scored 4 Test centuries at Lord's?

Century

15. Who at Old Trafford in 1993 became the first Australian for a hundred years to make his maiden first-class century in a Test match?

16. Name the only Australian not to be dismissed by Jim Laker when he took 19 wickets for England v Australia at Old Trafford.

17. Prior to 1994, when did England last win a Test match at the Kensington Oval in Bridgetown, Barbados?

18. When did Australia achieve their 100th Test match victory over England?

19. Name the three English batsmen to have made more than 1000 Test runs at Lord's.

20. Who was the only Lancashire player, before Mike Atherton, to score a Test match century at Old Trafford?

21. Who, at The Oval for India v England in 1990, bowled a Test record of 59 consecutive overs?

See Answers page 149

West Indies

*'Sabina Park in Jamaica is a sight to behold for a
visiting tourist – preferably from the dressing room
rather than out at the crease!'*

Quick single

22. Where did Frank Worrell and John Goddard put on 502 unbroken for the fourth wicket in 1943–44?

23. Which English player was refused entry to Guyana in 1980–81 causing the cancellation of the Test match at Bourda Oval, Georgetown?

24. Where was a Test match abandoned without a ball being bowled in the 1989–90 series in the West Indies?

25. Where did Lawrence Rowe score 302 v England in 1973–74?

26. Which was the most recent Test match ground in the West Indies?

27. On which Test match ground is the 'Three Ws' stand located?

28. What is the highest ever score made at Sabina Park, Kingston, Jamaica?

Half century

29. Which batsman scored the quickest century in a Test Match in terms of balls received?

30. Who took 8–45 in the Bridgetown Test between West Indies and England in 1989–90?

31. Who scored four centuries against the West Indies at Port of Spain, Trinidad?

32. On which ground did Conrad Hunte and Gary Sobers put on 446 for the second wicket v Pakistan in 1957–58?

33. Who achieved match figures of 13–156 in the West Indies v England and on which ground?

34. Which visiting Test batsman scored four centuries at Queen's Park Oval, Port of Spain, Trinidad between 1971 and 1976?

35. Who returned the best analysis by a West Indian fast bowler in Test cricket at Port of Spain v Pakistan in 1977?

Century

36. What is the highest score made by an English batsman in the West Indies? Name the batsman and the occasion.

37. Which England bowler v West Indies in Trinidad in 1989–90 took 10 wickets in a match against West Indies?

38. Where did George Headley make two centuries in a Test match in the West Indies?

39. Which bowler has returned the best ever analysis on the Bourda ground, Georgetown, Guyana in a Test match?

40. What is the name of the local Barbadian club side that plays at the Kensington Oval, Bridgetown?

41. Who scored the first Test match century on the Recreation Ground, St John's, Antigua?

42. On which ground in the West Indies was the first to host an English touring team in 1895 under the captaincy of R Slade Lucas?

See Answers page 150

Australia

'England's batsmen will certainly have to be wary of Shane Warne and Tim May in the Sydney Test for this winter's tour. The turning pitch at the SCG will be a real test.'

Quick single

43. Which cricket ground is nicknamed the 'Gabba'?

44. How many Test matches have Australia won at Lord's?

45. On which ground in Australia have the greatest number of Test matches been played?

46. In which year was an Ashes Test match abandoned without a ball being bowled in Australia and where was it?

47. On which Test match ground would the Brewongle Stand be found?

48. On which ground would you find the George Giffen Stand?

49. On which ground did R E Foster score his 287 which for almost 27 years was the world Test record score?

Half century

50. What is England's lowest Test score?

51. Which two players scored centuries in the tied Test between Australia and West Indies in Brisbane in 1960–61?

52. Which is the only Australian ground on which there have been two individual scores made of over 400?

53. What is the highest individual score ever made at the Sydney Cricket Ground?

54. Who made his England debut in the fourth Test of the series v Australia in 1970–71 at Sydney having been flown out as a replacement for Alan Ward?

55. Where was the last Test match hat-trick taken in Australia?

56. On which ground did Australia achieve its biggest victory by an innings against England?

Century

57. In 1928–29 England achieved her largest victory over Australia in terms of runs. How many and where was the Test match?

58. When and where did Warren Bardsley become the first Australian batsman to score a century in each innings in an Ashes Test?

59. In which Test match did England's last pair add 39 to win the match?

60. Which Australian batsman scored two centuries in a Test match v Pakistan in 1989–90 at Adelaide?

61. What is the highest individual innings in a Test match made by an Australian at Adelaide?

62. What is the highest individual innings in Ashes cricket scored on the Brisbane Exhibition Ground?

63. Who is the only Test player to score an Ashes double century at the Brisbane Woolloongabba Ground?

See Answers page 151

India, Pakistan and Sri Lanka

'Eden Gardens is an imposing ground unrivalled in the cricket world, apart perhaps from Melbourne. The sheer enthusiasm of the native Bengali for Test cricket is truly inspiring...'

Quick single

64. What was the name of the ground in Bombay used for Test matches prior to the building of the Wankhede Stadium in 1975?

65. Which ground was used by Pakistan for Test cricket prior to the secession of Bangladesh?

66. Where is the Chepauk Stadium?

67. In which city is Eden Gardens?

68. In which city is the Feroz Shah Kotla ground?

69. In which city is the Modi Stadium named after Rusi Modi the Indian batsman?

70. On which ground did Javed Miandad and Mudassar Nazar equal the Test third wicket partnership of 451 v India in 1983?

Half century

71. On which ground did Hanif Mohammad score his 499 v Bahawalpur in 1958–59?

72. On which ground did Bruce Taylor of New Zealand score his maiden in first class cricket in his first Test?

73. On which Indian Test ground did Kapil Dev take 9–83 v West Indies in 1983–84?

74. Who scored the first hundred in a Test match for India and on which ground?

75. Where and when was the only Test match in India captained by Gundappa Vishwanath?

76. On which Test match ground did Sunil Gavaskar score the highest ever score by an Indian batsman?

77. Which Pakistan bowler took 9–56 and 13–101 in the match v England at Lahore in 1987–88?

Century

78. Which Pakistan ground saw the first ever visit of a US President to a Test match ?

79. When did Brian Lara make his Test debut for West Indies, and how many did he score?

80. On which ground was the highest ever partnership of 577 recorded?

81. On which ground was Sri Lanka's first ever Test match played?

82. On which ground was the highest match aggregate recorded?

83. On which ground did Chetan Sharma take the only hat-trick in a World Cup match?

84. On which ground did Sunil Gavaskar and Dilip Vengsarkar put on 344 unbroken for the second wicket – the Indian record second partnership against all countries?

See Answers page 152

New Zealand

'New Plymouth is as picturesque a place for playing cricket as anywhere in the world, but the Test grounds are mostly rugby stadiums...specially sited for the wind-tunnel effect.'

Quick single

85. Where and when did New Zealand achieve their highest Test score against England?

86. On which ground did New Zealand play their first Test match?

87. Which three New Zealand batsmen scored centuries at Lord's against England in 1973?

88. On which ground did Walter Hammond score 336 not out in 1932–33 and exceed Don Bradman's 334, at that time the highest individual score in Test cricket?

89. Where did New Zealand play their first-ever Test match?

90. Which Test match ground staged the World Cup Rugby Union and Rugby League Finals in 1987 and 1988 respectively?

91. On which ground in February 1980 did New Zealand beat West Indies by one wicket?

Half century

92. Who took 11–147 (4–100 and 7–47) v New Zealand at Christchurch in 1991–92?

93. Where is McLean Park, which became the 50th Test match ground in 1978–79?

94. On which New Zealand ground did Frank Woolley take 7–76 for England in 1929–30, the best performance by an overseas player on this ground?

95. On which ground did Glenn Turner make his Test debut in 1968–69 and score his only 'duck' in Test cricket?

96. On which ground were England dismissed for 82 and 93, the only time this century that they have been dismissed under three figures in both innings of a Test, in 1984?

97. On which ground did Wasim Akram become the youngest bowler to take 10 wickets in a Test match at the age of 18 in 1984–85?

98. Who in his only Test match at Eden Park in Auckland in 1972–73 v Pakistan scored a century and a half century?

Century

99. Which England bowler in his first Test match v New Zealand at Christchurch in 1929–30 took four wickets in five balls?

100. On which ground in New Zealand did Bert Sutcliffe score 385 in the 1952–53 season?

101. On which ground did both sides score over 300 in a World Cup match?

102. A P Gurusinha and Andrew Jones both scored two separate hundreds in the same Test match – but on which ground?

103. Which New Zealand Test match ground was once known as the 'frog pond'?

104. The R A Vance Stand is on which ground?

105. Where were the headquarters of cricket in Christchurch prior to the move to Lancaster Park?

See Answers page 153

South Africa / Zimbabwe

'Newlands in Cape Town is the most perfect setting for any cricket ground in the world, with its oak trees lining one side and the magnificent Table Mountain looming in the distance.'

Quick single

106. What is the name of the ground on which South Africa achieved their highest Test score, and when did this happen?

107. In which city is the Kingsmead ground located?

108. On which ground was Zimbabwe's first Test match played?

109. On which ground did the 'Timeless' Test of 1938–39 take place?

110. In the last Test match played at Kingsmead, Durban before South Africa's isolation in 1969–70 who scored the highest ever individual score for South Africa in Test cricket?

111. Which bowler returned the best figures on the New Wanderers ground in Johannesburg in a Test match?

112. Which was Graeme Pollock's home ground?

Half century

113. On which ground did Denis Compton score the fastest triple hundred?

114. Which Australian batsman scored Test match centuries on all four South African Test grounds in 1949–50?

115. Which is South Africa's oldest Test ground dating from 1889?

116. Where in South Africa was the Lord's ground?

117. Which was the first venue in South Africa to produce a turf pitch for Test cricket in 1931?

118. Who in the first Test match to be played at the Old Wanderers ground in Johannesburg in 1896 returned figures of 8–7 for England?

119. Who made the first Test century for South Africa at Newlands Cape Town in 1899?

Century

120. Which South African scored 142 out of a total of 196 in a Test match at Lord's?

121. Who hit his highest score for Orange Free State v Eastern Province at Bloemfontein in 1987–88?

122. On which ground was the last century made for South Africa prior to isolation in the 1969–70 series?

123. What is unusual about the Old Wanderers cricket ground in Johannesburg?

124. On which ground in South Africa was the lowest aggregate total in a completed first-class match achieved?

125. Bobby Abel of Surrey made the first ever Test century in South Africa in 1889. On which ground was it made?

126. Who at Kingsmead, Durban in 1922–23 became the first player to score a century in both innings of a Test match in South Africa?

See Answers page 154

CHAPTER 6

Cricket Records

England v Australia

'I never really was one for records, but I am proud to have scored over 3,000 runs against Australia in Test cricket.'

Quick single

1. Who scored the most runs for Australia in the 1993 Test series v England?

2. Who scored the most runs for England in the 1993 Test series?

3. Which English bowler took the most wickets in the series v Australia in 1993?

4. Which Australian batsman's only three centuries against England have all exceeded 150 and been unbeaten?

5. Which Australian batsman scored three centuries in successive tests v England in 1993?

6. Who reached 1,000 runs in Ashes Tests in his seventh Test and thirteenth innings?

7. When was the only occasion that three batsmen reached 500 runs in a series in Ashes Test matches?

Half century

8. In which series against Australia did England use the greatest number of players?

9. When and where were two Ashes Test matches abandoned without a ball being bowled?

10. What is the longest period, in terms of matches, in which England have failed to beat Australia?

11. Which cricketer represented England against Australia at Lord's in 1993 and announced his retirement from first-class cricket after playing only one further match?

12. Which wicketkeeper has played the greatest number of Ashes Tests?

13. On how many occasions has Australia won four Test matches in a series in England and when?

14. Who scored the greatest number of runs for England in the 1989 series v Australia?

Century

15. Which player remained scoreless for 72 minutes for Australia v England at Sydney in 1990–91 and was ultimately dismissed for 9 after 107 minutes?

16. Who was the first player to make a century on his debut for England?

17. Who is the oldest player to make a maiden Test match hundred?

18. Who are the only five players to have played for both Australia and England?

19. Who are the only two players in England v Australia Test matches to be dismissed in the 90s in both innings?

20. What is the biggest opening partnership for Australia in Test cricket?

21. Which player has scored the greatest number of runs and the greatest number of centuries for England v Australia?

See Answers page 155

Triple-centuries

*'A first-class triple-century proved to be beyond my grasp,
although I was suitably proud of my 228 for
Leicestershire in 1989.'*

Quick single

22. Which Australian scored 345 in a day v Nottinghamshire in
    1921?

23. Which player scored 312 not out for MCC Under-25s v
    North Zone at Peshawar in 1966–67?

24. Which Kent and England player made 307 for MCC v South
    Australia at Adelaide in 1962–63, the highest score of his
    career?

25. What is the highest first-class score ever made by a South
    African batsman?

26. Which Victorian left-hander scored 307 for Australia v
    England at Melbourne in 1965–66?

27. Who scored the first-ever triple-century in first-class cricket?

28. Who in scoring 337 played the longest innings in first-class
    cricket?

Half century

29. Who held the record score for Warwickshire prior to its
    eclipse by Brian Lara in 1994?

30. What was the highest score in the County Championship this
    century before Brian Lara's 501 not out?

31. Which Worcestershire batsman scored 311 not out against Warwickshire at Worcester in 1982?

32. Who scored 304 not out in a total of 730–3 v Cambridge University in 1950?

33. What is the highest score ever made for Middlesex, and by whom?

34. Who exceeded 300 on six occasions in his career?

35. Which two batsmen scored triple-centuries on the same day in county cricket?

Century

36. Who, prior to Brian Lara in the fifth Test in Antigua for West Indies v England in April 1994, had scored the most recent triple-century in first-class cricket?

37. What is the highest first-class score ever made in South Africa and by whom?

38. Who scored a triple-century at the 1986 Scarborough Cricket Festival?

39. Who scored 355 not out for Western Australia v South Australia in 1989–90?

40. Which player scored over 400 in a first-class match yet never played Test cricket?

41. Who are the only two batsmen to have made triple-centuries in the same innings?

42. Who made 312 not out for Nottinghamshire at The Oval but was playing against Middlesex?

See Answers page 156

County Championship

'From his first introduction to Test cricket, Brian Lara always looked a cut above the rest and destined for cricket's record books. Of course, it helps being a left-hander...'

Quick single

43. Which bowler has taken the highest aggregate of first-class cricket wickets in a season?

44. Which cricketer has hit the greatest number of sixes in a season?

45. Who is the only cricketer to score two double-hundreds in the same match?

46. Which batsman in 1994 scored the slowest century in the history of the County Championship?

47. Who has scored the greatest number of first-class hundreds in a season, and how many?

48. Which bowler took 7 wickets in 11 balls against Sussex at Eastbourne in 1972?

49. Who was the first player to make 3,000 runs in an English first-class season?

Half century

50. Which county won their only championship in 1936?

51. Which current wicketkeeper has taken the greatest number of victims in first-class cricket?

52. Who topped the batting averages for the 1994 season?

53. Which former Northamptonshire player, currently playing for Yorkshire, went 12 consecutive innings without scoring a run?

54. Name the only two players since the Second World War to score 1,000 runs in English first-class cricket before the end of May.

55. Which batsman has scored the greatest number of runs in a day?

56. Name the two players who hold the English first-wicket partnership of 555 v Essex.

Century

57. What is the greatest percentage of a tenth wicket stand for one partner to have provided?

58. What is the lowest score to include two individual centuries in a first-class match?

59. Who is the youngest player to take over a hundred wickets in his debut season?

60. Which batsman scored 1,000 runs in a season on 23 occasions and did not play an official Test match for England?

61. Who was the last Englishman to take four wickets in four balls?

62. Which player achieved two separate hat-tricks in the same innings of his benefit match?

63. Who was the last player to take a hat-trick on his first-class debut?

See Answers page 157

Touring Teams to England

'Mark Taylor loves English conditions and it was no surprise to see him rewrite the record books on the 1989 Australian tour to these shores.'

Quick single

64. What is the greatest number of runs scored in a day, and where?

65. Which Australian batsman scored nine centuries on the tour of England in 1993?

66. For which county did E A 'Ted' Macdonald, of the famous Gregory and Macdonald Australian fast bowling partnership, play county cricket?

67. Which Australian batsman scored over 1,000 runs on the 1993 tour of England at an average of 57.50 but failed to be selected for any of the Test matches?

68. What is the lowest score made by the Australians in a first-class match on a tour of England?

69. Who were the first county to beat the South African tourists on their tour of England in 1994?

70. Who scored the only double-century of the South African tour of England in 1994?

Half century

71. Who, playing for Pakistan v Glamorgan at Swansea in 1967, scored 13 sixes in an innings?

72. What is the highest score ever made by the South Africans against an English county?

73. Who are the only two Australians to achieve the double three times on tours of England?

74. Who scored 201 not out in 120 minutes against Glamorgan at Swansea in 1976?

75. What was the highest score made against the 1993 Australian touring team to England, and by whom was it scored?

76. Who was the first Australian to score a triple-century whilst on tour to England?

77. Which Australian hit 12 sixes in an innings v Warwickshire at Birmingham in 1989?

Century

78. What is the highest average ever recorded by a West Indian on a tour of England?

79. When was the first occasion that twins scored centuries for opposing teams in first-class cricket?

80. What was the highest score ever made by Don Bradman at Lord's?

81. Who dismissed the Australian batsman Mark Taylor with his first ball in first-class cricket?

82. Who was the Tasmanian selected as second wicketkeeper for the Australian tour of England in 1890 who, it was discovered after the ship had sailed, had never kept wicket in his life?

83. Who took the first hat-trick by an Australian tourist since 1912, playing against Derbyshire at Derby in 1993?

84. Who is the only Australian tourist to score a hundred and take a hat-trick on a tour of England?

See Answers page 158

All first-class cricket

'I wonder if Ravi Shastri ever thought he would repeat Gary Sobers' feat of hitting six sixes in one over – certainly a remarkable achievement.'

Quick single

85. Which batsman scored the greatest number of centuries in his career?

86. Which three current batsmen have scored more than 40,000 runs?

87. Who is the youngest person to score 50 first-class 100s?

88. Who has taken the greatest number of hat-tricks in a first-class career?

89. Who is the only West Indian to score 100 hundreds?

90. Which two batsmen from the same county scored 7,355 runs between them in first-class cricket in one season, and when?

91. Which England wicketkeeper/batsman played 47 Test matches and scored 102 centuries in first-class cricket?

Half century

92. Which batsmen have scored six successive hundreds in first-class cricket?

93. What is the record first-wicket partnership in first-class cricket?

94. Which four batsmen have averaged over 100 in an English season?

95. Which current batsman has the highest aggregate of runs in first-class cricket?

96. Which bowler three times in his career took 10 wickets in an innings?

97. Which two players scored 1,000 runs in a season most times?

98. Who was the second player to hit 36 runs off one over?

Century

99. In which match were there three scores of more than 200 in the same innings for the first time in cricket history?

100. What is the highest score by a batsman on his first-class debut?

101. Name the only bowler twice to have taken four wickets in four balls.

102. Which batsmen have scored six hundreds in seven innings?

103. What is the highest total in first-class cricket?

104. Who has taken the greatest number of wickets in first-class cricket?

105. Who, on four separate occasions, has scored a double-hundred and a hundred in the same match without being dismissed?

See Answers page 159

Test records

'I played the game because it was fun, rather than as a quest for getting my name into the record books.'

Quick single

106. Who are the only two batsmen to have scored 10,000 runs in Tests?

107. Which bowler has taken the greatest number of wickets in a first-class match?

108. Which much-loved cricketer, who scored 6,806 runs at an average of 58.67 and became England tour manager, died during the West Indies tour in 1980–81?

109. Which South African scored a century in the Lord's Test match v England in 1994?

110. What is the lowest score ever made by England in a Test Match v South Africa?

111. Who is the only Australian to have scored 100 hundreds in first-class cricket?

112. What is the highest aggregate of runs ever made in a Test series?

Half century

113. Who bowled 137 consecutive balls in a Test match without conceding a run?

114. Which bowler bowled the most balls in a Test match?

115. Which TV commentator was the first cricketer to score 2,000 runs and take 200 wickets in Test cricket?

116. Who was the last bowler to take a wicket with his first ball in Test cricket?

117. Which four players still playing first-class cricket have received only one England Test cap in their careers?

118. Who is the Australian batsman to have been dismissed five times in the 'nervous nineties' in Tests against England?

119. What is the highest score made by a West Indian in a Test match v Australia?

Century

120. How many Test match players have batted in more than 200 innings and who are they?

121. Which batsman has scored the greatest number of runs before lunch on the first day of a Test match?

122. Who are the only three batsmen to score six or more double-centuries in Test cricket?

123. Which two batsmen put on 451 for the third wicket at Hyderabad in 1982–83 v India to equal the record partnership for any wicket in Test cricket?

124. Who was the oldest Test debutant in the 20th century?

125. Who are the four English players to have taken more than 100 catches in Test cricket?

126. Who was England's oldest ever Test debutant?

See Answers page 161

CHAPTER 7

Other Cricket

University and School Cricket

'University cricket has never really been the extensive breeding ground for the next generation of England Test players, although some, like Mike Atherton, have made it to the very top.'

Quick single

1. Who was the captain of Oxford University in the 1993 University Match, and now plays for Lancashire?

2. Which undergraduate scored a hundred for Combined Universities v Australia at Oxford in 1993?

3. When was the Eton v Harrow Match first played at Lord's?

4. Who scored the only century for Cambridge University in 1993 and was selected to play Test cricket for England in 1994?

5. Who in 1994 became the second Bradman scholar at Oxford University on a cricket scholarship?

6. Who in 1993 scored his 100th first class century against Cambridge University and retired out for 105?

7. Which University side won the UAU Championship for four consecutive years between 1990 and 1993?

Half century

8. The son of which former Chelsea and England footballer played cricket for Oxford University in 1994?

9. Which Oxford University bowler took 10–104 in the 1994 University match?

10. Who were the winners of the Commercial Union UAU Championship final in 1994?

11. Who made the most runs in a career for Cambridge University?

12. Which Cambridge captain dropped out of the University match at Lord's in order to play a Test match for England?

13. Who was the first recipient of a Bradman Scholarship to attend Oxford University from 1990–93?

14. Which three players scored centuries for Oxford in 1993?

Century

15. Which two batsmen scored centuries for Oxford in the 1994 University match?

16. Who is the only batsman to score a hundred in each innings of the University match?

17. When was the first University match between Oxford and Cambridge?

18. What is the highest score ever made in the University match at Lord's?

19. Who performed the hat-trick by taking the last three wickets to win the 1870 University match for Cambridge by two runs – a feat unparalleled in first-class cricket?

20. Which two undergraduates in 1950 had an opening stand of 343 v West Indies for Cambridge University?

21. When was the last time that Harrow won a one-day game against Eton?

See Answers page 162

England A / Minor Counties / Women's Cricket / 2nd XI Cricket / Under-19s

'Alan Wells fully deserves the captaincy of this winter's 'A' tour to India, despite a poor season with Sussex.'

Quick single

22. Who are the sponsors of the County 2nd XI Championship?

23. Who won the Minor Counties Championship for the third consecutive year in 1993?

24. Who won the MCC Trophy in 1994?

25. Who did England beat in the final of the Women's World Cup at Lord's in 1993?

26. Who was Player of the Match in the Women's World Cup Final at Lord's?

27. Who was captain of the England 'A' team to tour West Indies and Bermuda in 1991–92?

28. Which player captained the Under-19s side v India in 1994 and was selected for the England 'A' tour to India in 1994–95?

Half century

29. Which was the first minor county to beat a first-class county in the Gillette Cup?

30. Who captained the England 'A' team to Zimbabwe in 1989–90?

31. Which batsman on the 1993–94 England 'A' tour of South Africa scored 779 runs in first-class matches, at 64.92?

32. Who took the greatest number of wickets on England 'A's tour of South Africa in 1993–94?

33. Which country won the ICC Trophy in 1994?

34. Which England captain was made an OBE in the New Year's Honours, 1994?

35. Who won the ICC Trophy in 1990?

Century

36. Name the first minor county to reach the quarter-finals of the Gillette Cup.

37. Which minor country won a match in 1994 totalling 484 in their two innings, without losing a wicket?

38. Who toured with the 1964 Australian Touring team without playing a Test match and later suffered a fractured skull whilst playing for the Australians against Holland?

39. Who scored 221 for England 'A' v Zimbabwe in Bulawayo in 1989–90?

40. Who were the two players to score centuries on the England 'A' Tour to Sri Lanka in 1990–91 in the unofficial five-day Test matches?

41. Who, other than Shivnarine Chanderpaul, scored a double century in the Under-19 series between England and West Indies?

42. Who scored a double-century for England Under-19s in the third Test Match at Edgbaston v India in 1994?

See Answers page 163

Controversy

'Being of a slightly rebellious nature, the selectors cut me adrift after the 1990–91 series in Australia.'

Quick single

43. Where was an England v Australia Test match abandoned due to vandalism?

44. Which England batsman in a Test match in Australia smashed the stumps down with his bat after being bowled for 139?

45. Who resigned from the ICC's Cricket Committee after admitting ball tampering?

46. Who captained the first 'rebel' tour to South Africa?

47. Which fellow aviator of David Gower scored the first double-century for Durham in first-class cricket?

48. Whose selection for the proposed England tour to South Africa in 1968–69 caused the cancellation of the tour and the expulsion of South Africa from Test cricket?

49. Which England captain, in 1976, stated he wanted his opponents to 'grovel'?

Half century

50. Which Pakistani fast bowler was accused by Allan Lamb of 'cheating' (ball tampering), leading to a High Court action against the latter?

51. Which cricketer took 10–70 and scored 53 in his first Test match for England, and was accused of using vaseline to maintain the shine on the ball?

52. Which bowler, having taken a hat-trick in a Test match at Lord's, was later no-balled for throwing in an exhibition match following the Test?

53. Who was refused entry to Guyana when touring with England, due to his South African connections, which resulted in the cancellation of a Test match?

54. Which team in 1994 received a 25-point penalty for producing a pitch completely unsuitable for the start of a first-class match?

55. At which Test match venue was fusarium disease blamed for a sub-standard wicket for an England v Australia Test match?

56. In which Ashes Test match did the England captain Ray Illingworth lead his team from the field after a spectator attacked John Snow?

Century

57. In which Test match was the greatest number of lbws?

58. Who, in 1992–93, was the first player to be suspended under the International Code of Conduct?

59. Name the captain who declared his side's innings closed before facing a ball, to ensure qualification for the knockout stages of the Benson and Hedges Cup?

60. Which two counties in the 1989 English season were docked 25 points for preparing sub-standard pitches?

61. Which was the year that the Lord's pitch for a Test match was affected by cranefly larvae?

62. Which ex-Lancashire and Derbyshire cricketer died shortly after being hit in the face whilst batting in 1993?

63. Which West Indian cricketer deviated in his run-up to charge into umpire Fred Goodall in a Test match v New Zealand in February 1980 at Christchurch?

Selectors/Umpires/ Administrators

'I was fortunate in having Ray Illingworth as my mentor at Leicestershire.'

Quick single

64. Which former Leicestershire captain became Chairman of the Test selectors in 1994?

65. Who was Chairman of the Test selectors prior to Ted Dexter, and retired from the job in 1988–89?

66. Which former Yorkshire and England cricketer, and MCC Coach, is now Director of Sport at Ampleforth College?

67. Which umpire has officiated in the greatest number of Test matches?

68. What was the name of the Pakistan umpire involved in the confrontation with Mike Gatting on the England tour of 1987–88?

69. Which current first-class and Test match umpire took 1–189 on his Test debut v South Africa in 1964–65 at Port Elizabeth?

70. Who, apart from Raymond Illingworth, are the other current England selectors?

Half century

71. Who became the first overseas umpire to stand in a Test in England?

72. Which player, who represented England in ten limited-overs internationals, was capped by three countries and then became a first-class umpire?

73. Which leading Leicestershire figure, having joined the club as a leg-spinner in 1951, resigned as Chief Executive in 1993?

74. Who is the chief coach to the Australian Cricket Academy in Adelaide?

75. Who is the full-time Chief Executive of the International Cricket Council?

76. Who succeeded Clive Lloyd as Manager of the West Indies in 1990?

77. Which former England fast bowler became the Surrey bowling coach in 1994.

Century

78. Which was the first Test series to feature neutral umpires?

79. Against whom did Ted Dexter, as a Conservative, stand for Parliament at Cardiff South-east in 1964?

80. Which Worcestershire captain, now Northamptonshire's cricket manager, played professional football for Lincoln City under the former England football manager Graham Taylor?

81. Which umpire has made the greatest number of County Championship appearances?

82. What was the name of the umpire who was ragged by the MCC 'A' team to Pakistan in 1955–56 threatening the continuation of the tour?

83. Which umpire no-balled Willsher six times in succession in a match between Surrey and England in 1862?

84. Which umpire was responsible for calling the South African Geoff Giffin for throwing at Lord's in 1960?

See Answers page 165

All-rounders

'Ian Botham was the best all-rounder I ever played with or against – I wouldn't want him as an opponent too often!'

Quick single

85. Who on the England tour to India in 1992–93 was England's leading run-scorer, wicket-taker, and catcher?

86. Which celebrated England all-rounder played in a winning side on his 20th Test match appearance against the West Indies?

87. Who is the only Englishman to have scored more than 2000 runs and taken more than 100 wickets in one-day internationals?

88. Who are the only two Australians to have scored 1,000 runs and taken 100 wickets in limited-over internationals?

89. Who is the youngest and only player in his debut season to achieve the double of 1000 runs and 100 wickets?

90. Which three post war players achieved 20,000 runs and 2000 wickets in a career?

91. How many times did Ian Botham achieve a century and five wickets in an innings in Test cricket?

Half century

92. What is the fastest double of 1000 runs and 100 wickets in England v Australia Tests?

93. Which Australian Test cricketer who played in the 1946–47 series later played county cricket for Nottinghamshire and twice achieved the double?

94. Who achieved the double of 200 Test wickets and 2000 runs in the quickest time?

95. Which player scored more than 50,000 runs and took more than 2,500 wickets?

96. Who played 25 Test matches for England but never scored 1000 runs or took 100 wickets in a season?

97. Who took 200 wickets and scored 2,000 runs in a season?

98. Name the only two wicketkeepers to have scored more than 1000 runs and made 100 dismissals in limited-overs cricket.

Century

99. Which overseas players achieved the double the greatest number of times?

100. Which three players have scored 100 runs and taken ten wickets in a Test?

101. Who are the only two players to have achieved the treble of 1000 runs, 100 wickets and 100 catches in Test cricket?

102. Who was the first player to attain the double of 1000 Test runs and 200 Test wickets?

103. Who, in 1964, won an FA Cup winner's medal, a County Championship winner's medal, and topped the national bowling averages?

104. Who was batting at the other end when Denis Compton played his maiden first-class innings for Middlesex on 1 June 1936?

105. Name the only three players to have scored 1000 runs and taken 200 wickets in a season?

See Answers page 166

Literature/Journalism

'It took a lot of "mind over matter" getting my autobiography together. Some were even surprised at the things I said...'

Quick single

106. Which Leicestershire and England cricketer retired at the end of 1990 to become a cricket correspondent, and is now the BBC Cricket Correspondent?

107. Which England cricketer retired at the end of 1993 to become Cricket Correspondent for the *Independent on Sunday*?

108. Which former Somerset captain is Cricket Correspondent for *The Sunday Times* and Captain of Devon?

109. Which celebrated cricket writer was created CBE in 1964 and knighted in 1967?

110. Which writer wrote *Cricketers of My Time* in 1833 and *The Young Cricketer's Tutor*?

111. Which Somerset player bowled Bradman for 202 and subsequently titled his autobiography *The Hand that Bowled Bradman*?

112. Which West Indian, socialist, philosopher wrote *Beyond a Boundary*?

Half century

113. Which celebrated cricket writer was made a CBE in the 1994 New Year's Honours List?

114. Which celebrated leg-spinner called his autobiography *10 for 66 And All That* in 1958?

115. Whose biography was entitled *Farewell to Cricket*?

116. Who is the current editor of the *Wisden Cricketers' Almanack*?

117. Which former Jamaican Prime Minister wrote *A History of West Indies Cricket*?

118. Which cricket writer and journalist was nicknamed 'Crusoe'?

119. Who founded *The Cricketer* magazine in 1921?

Century

120. Who is the only Nobel Prize winner to have played first-class cricket?

121. In which book did Dingly Dell meet All Muggleton, and who was the author?

122. Which celebrated English playwright, and in which play, names his two leading characters after the two major figures of the Golden Age of Cricket, and who were they?

123. Who in 1851 published *The Cricket Field* based on the memoirs of William Fennex?

124. Which cricket writer and journalist was known as 'Old Ebor'?

125. Who was Felix who wrote *Felix on the Bat* published in 1845?

126. Whose honorary life membership was withdrawn after publication of his autobiography *Over to Me* in 1960?

See Answers page 167

CHAPTER 8

General Knowledge/Trivia

Trivia 1

'The only time I have ever played cricket in South Africa was on a schools' tour with "The Crocodiles", captained by Chris Cowdrey in the mid seventies. At the time of the rebel tour in 1982, my main ambitions were centred on playing for England for as long as possible.'

Quick single

1. Which current Australian batsman, other than Michael Slater, comes from Wagga Wagga, New South Wales?

2. What is the record number of successive defeats by an England Test team?

3. In 1978 David Gower pulled his first ball in Test cricket for four – who was the bowler?

4. When, and against whom, did David Gower make his Test match debut?

5. Which South African player ran out two batsmen with direct hits in the Lord's Test of 1965, and who were they?

6. Who were the three batsmen recalled successfully to play in the 1956 home series v Australia?

7. How many Test matches did David Gower play in his career between 1978 and 1992?

Half century

8. Who was the first man in Test cricket to score a 5 by hitting the fielder's helmet?

9. Which England left-hander averages 15.64 for ten Test matches and 40.13 for 40 one-day internationals?

10. Which batsman was at the non-striker's end when both Geoff Boycott and John Edrich scored their 100th centuries in 1977?

11. Which Test cricketer in 1990 made 1058 Test runs in 68 days?

12. Name the only player to be given out obstructed the field in a Test match.

13. Which bowler has the best strike rate in the history of Test cricket?

14. Which batsman had the greatest number of consecutive Test innings without a duck?

Century

15. Who was the 500th cricketer to represent England in their 586th Test match?

16. Who scored the 100th Test century for Australia in Tests against England?

17. Who was the first player to score a century in each innings of a Test match?

18. What is the overall record for remaining scoreless in Test cricket?

19. Which wicketkeeper holds the world record of not conceding a bye for the highest number of runs?

20. Which two Indian Test batsmen, in 1987–88, put on 664 unbroken for the third wicket for Sharadashram Vidyamandis School v St Xavier's High School in Bombay in 1987–88?

21. What is the highest tenth wicket stand in first-class cricket?

See Answers page 168

Trivia 2

'Over-rates have become quite a problem in the modern game and professionalism has played an increasing role in this. Don Bradman would never be able to score 300 in a Test match in the present era.'

Quick single

22. Whose Test debut coincided with David Gower's 100th Test match?

23. In which year did England play Test cricket concurrently against two different opponents?

24. Which batsman has scored the greatest number of double-centuries in his career?

25. Who received the first knighthood to be conferred on a professional cricketer?

26. Which county ground, used since 1872, ceased to be used as a first-class venue in 1989?

27. Which batsman has scored two separate hundreds in a match the greatest number of times?

28. Which Australian State team has never won the Sheffield Shield?

Half century

29. Which cricketer scored 1000 runs in 28 consecutive seasons between 1907 and 1938?

30. Who once scored 35 in 332 minutes for England in a Test match?

31. Who is the only player to score 99 not out in a Test match?

32. Who has taken the greatest number of wickets in first-class cricket?

33. Who took 8–2 in a Test trial for England v The Rest at Bradford in 1950?

34. Who were the two batsmen to score 1,000 runs before the end of May 1938?

35. Who are the only two batsmen to reach 1000 first-class runs in seven innings?

Century

36. What is the highest winning score made this century in a fourth innings to win a first-class match?

37. Which players scored ten 50s in consecutive innings?

38. Who has taken the greatest number of wickets in the Sheffield Shield?

39. What is the record aggregate number of runs scored in the Ranji Trophy and by whom?

40. Who has the highest average by an English player now retired who has scored more than 10,000 career runs?

41. Which bowler holds the record for the greatest number of wickets in a South African first-class domestic season?

42. Who scored a century in the last Gentleman v Players match at Scarborough in 1962?

See Answers page 170

Trivia 3

'It seems a pity that when on tour, runs round the block count for more than runs in the middle.'

Quick single

43. Which State won the 1993–94 Castle Cup competition in South Africa?

44. Which first-class cricketer scored a hat-trick in a World Cup football final?

45. Which is the country most recently to claim Test match status, and when?

46. Which three batsmen were known as the 'Three Ws'?

47. Which two West Indians were known as 'Those two little pals of mine'?

48. In which year was *Wisden Cricketers' Almanack* first published?

49. Who is Sunil Gavaskar's brother-in-law?

Half century

50. What is the record number of runs scored by a batsman in the Red Stripe Competition (the West Indies domestic first-class competition) and who was the batsman?

51. Who made the highest-ever score in an organized cricket match, and what was the score?

52. Which Australian cricketer completed a sequence of six centuries in seven innings in the Sheffield Shield in 1993–94?

53. Which was the first Test match to feature TV replays to assist the umpires in close decisions?

54. Which current England cricketer played soccer for England v Scotland Schoolboys?

55. In which city was the Bramall Lane ground where a Test match was staged in 1902?

56. Who, in 1992, hit a ball over the lime tree at Canterbury?

Century

57. Which county twice conceded 81 extras in the 1994 season?

58. Name the South African player who was injured and returned home before playing a match on the 1994 Tour of England.

59. Which Australian bowler was no-balled 19 times in his first three overs during his first appearance in England?

60. Who was the first South African to score 150 in both innings of a match?

61. Who are the three players to score over 1,000 runs in five consecutive Test matches?

62. What is the greatest number of runs scored in a calendar month in first-class cricket?

63. Which four English batsmen have scored three successive Test centuries?

See Answers page 171

Trivia 4

'It is difficult to maintain individuality when so much emphasis is put on work rate.'

Quick single

64. What is the name of the trophy awarded for the fastest first-class century of the season?

65. Who was the first man to hit four consecutive sixes in one Test over?

66. Name the only player to score a triple century and a hundred in the same match?

67. Who was the first Hong Kong born player to appear in Test cricket?

68. Who is the youngest Test cricketer to play for England?

69. Which England bowler took his 100th Test wicket v New Zealand at Trent Bridge?

70. Who, having made 10 not out on his Test debut as an opener, was injured and played no further Test cricket?

Half century

71. When did India win their first Test series in England and who was the captain?

72. What is the record aggregate in a Lord's Test match?

73. What is the lowest total ever recorded in a Test match, and who by?

74. When was the last occasion a Test match was won by one wicket?

75. Who was the last Englishman to take a Test match hat-trick?

76. Who was the first black player to represent England in a Test match?

77. Who was the first batsman to score a triple-century in a Test match, and also the oldest?

Century

78. What is the greatest number of dismissals by a wicketkeeper in a Test match?

79. Which two batsmen compiled successive opening partnerships of over 200 in successive Tests for the first time in Test history?

80. Who was seriously injured, having been run over by an airport baggage truck at Heathrow, but four years later scored a Test century at Lord's?

81. Which player, in his only Test match for England, stood at slip for three hours at which point it rained for the rest of the match, leaving him as the only player never to have batted, bowled, or dismissed anyone in the field?

82. Who scored the first century for Zimbabwe in Test cricket?

83. Who is the oldest player to have played Test cricket?

84. Who is the only man to carry his bat through a Test innings on three occasions?

See Answers page 172

Trivia 5

'During my career there is little doubt that the game has become nastier, both physically and verbally...'

Quick single

85. Which Middlesex and England player died whilst batting in The Gambia in 1989?

86. Who was the first bowler to take 300 Test wickets?

87. Which player has played the greatest number of Test matches for England?

88. Who took 8–51 v Pakistan at Lord's in 1974?

89. Who has taken the greatest number of Test wickets for South Africa?

90. Which celebrated England batsman managed only 53 runs in eight innings on the 1950–51 Ashes series?

91. Which batsman scored 48,426 runs in first-class cricket with 151 centuries and 8,114 runs in Tests?

Half century

92. Who in 1980–81 was refused entry to Guyana resulting in the cancellation of the West Indies v England Test in Georgetown?

93. Who was the last England batsman to carry his bat through a Test innings?

94. Which two batsmen put on 63 opening stands of 100 or more for Surrey?

95. Who was the England bowler who took 4 wickets in 5 balls v Pakistan at Birmingham in 1978?

96. What is the highest score for South Africa against England in a Test match?

97. Who is the only batsman to score four successive Test 100s against England?

98. Which two England bowlers bowled South Africa out for 30 at Edgbaston in 1924?

Century

99. Which Surrey bowler took 112 wickets in his 118 Tests at an average of 10.75?

100. Which player has scored the slowest-ever century in Test cricket?

101. Which two opposing captains each scored centuries in successive Test matches?

102. Which player took four wickets in an over v South Africa in 1947?

103. Who took England's last hat-trick against South Africa?

104. Which celebrated Hollywood film star captained England in a Test match against South Africa, taking 7–61 in the match at Port Elizabeth in 1888–89?

105. Which England batsman scrambled a leg-bye off the last ball of the match v South Africa at Durban in 1948–49 to give England a two-wicket victory?

See Answers page 173

Trivia 6

'Mike Atherton is an intelligent bloke who knows what makes me tick and what doesn't. We get on well.'

Quick single

106. Which county were bowled out for 14, and by whom, in 1983?

107. Where was the first Test match played?

108. Which two England players were both educated at Willesden High School in North London?

109. Which fast bowler was forced to retire from first-class cricket in 1993 after breaking a knee cap playing for England in New Zealand?

110. What is England's lowest Test score v West Indies?

111. Who returned to Test cricket in the West Indies in 1989–90, nine years after his previous appearance?

112. Who, at the Lord's Test in 1984, led the West Indies to victory (chasing 342 to win by nine wickets) by scoring 214 not out?

Half century

113. What is the highest fourth innings winning total made by England in a Test match?

114. Who are the four English Test cricketers to take 100 catches in Test cricket?

115. Which fielder has taken the most catches in a first-class match?

116. Name the only English batsman to have been dismissed obstructed the field in a Test match?

117. Which batsman during the final month of the 1994 season averaged 854 runs per innings, having only been dismissed once during that period?

118. Who is the oldest English cricketer to score a Test double-century?

119. Name the only three players, prior to Alec Stewart, to score a century in each innings of a Test match against the West Indies.

Century

120. Which player scored the greatest number of runs before lunch in a Test match?

121. Who scored the only century of his career in a Test match?

122. Who is the oldest cricketer to score a Test double-century?

123. Who made the fastest authentic hundred in first-class cricket in terms of balls received?

124. What is the greatest number of runs conceded by a bowler in an innings in first-class cricket?

125. Who took 2,356 wickets, captained England four times, and made his first tour to Australia in 1928–29 aged 37, taking 25 Test wickets?

126. When was the first occasion in Test history that four batsmen were dismissed in the 90s?

See Answers page 174

Answers

ANSWERS FOR CHAPTER 1

England Test Cricket

Debuts

1. Graham Gooch.
2. Graham Thorpe, 114 not out at Trent Bridge.
3. Mark Lathwell, Graham Thorpe, Martin McCague and Mark Ilott.
4. A C S 'Tony' Pigott.
5. John Crawley.
6. Archie McLaren in 1909.
7. Joey Benjamin.

8. Ian Healy v England (1st Test) at Nottingham.
9. Charles Bannerman of Australia 165.
10. Dirk Wellham 103.
11. James Whittaker of Leicestershire.
12. 108 v England at Perth in 1970–71.
13. Syd Lawrence and Jack Russell.
14. J H 'John' Childs in 1988.

15. Dr Roy Park for Australia v England at Melbourne in 1920–21.
16. R W 'Bob' Barber.
17. J Hardstaff Jnr.
18. R C 'Jack' Russell.
19. Geoff Cook of Northamptonshire.
20. J H 'Jackie' Hampshire, 107 England v West Indies in 1969.
21. S C 'Billy' Griffith, 149 v West Indies at Port of Spain, Trinidad, in 1947–48.

Partnerships

22. Steve Waugh, 157 not out; Border 200 not out. The second highest fifth wicket partnership in Test cricket history.
23. Ian and Greg Chappell.
24. Peter May and Colin Cowdrey v West Indies at Birmingham in 1957.
25. Fred Titmus.
26. Mike Atherton, Alec Stewart and Graham Gooch.
27. Jack Hobbs – 16.
28. 130 by Wilfred Rhodes and R E Foster at Sydney in 1903–4.

29. The Oval in 1985 – 351 for the second wicket, G A Gooch 196 and D I Gower 157.
30. Geoff Marsh and Mark Taylor, 329 at Nottingham in 1989.
31. 323 by Wilfred Rhodes and Jack Hobbs at Melbourne in 1911–12.
32. George Hirst and Wilfred Rhodes.
33. Nottingham, 1989.
34. Graham Dilley.
35. Gary Sobers 163 not out, and David Holford 106 not out.

36. Sid Barnes and Don Bradman for Australia v England at Sydney in 1946–47.
37. Geoff Boycott and Alan Knott.
38. 369 for 2nd wicket by John Edrich 310 not out, and Ken Barrington 163 at Headingley in 1965.
39. 359 v South Africa at Johannesburg in 1948–49.
40. England v West Indies at The Oval in 1966. 217 for the 8th wicket by Tom Graveney and John Murray, 128 for the 10th wicket by Ken Higgs and John Snow.
41. Jack Hobbs and Herbert Sutcliffe.
42. Len Hutton and Cyril Washbrook at Adelaide in 1946–47 and Leeds in 1948.

Batsmen

43. 215 v Australia at Edgbaston in 1985.
44. Len Hutton, 364, England v Australia, 1938.
45. Mark Waugh of Australia and Mike Atherton of England at Lord's.
46. Tim Robinson 148; Mike Gatting 100 not out.
47. Graham Gooch, England v Australia (1st Test match), Old Trafford, Manchester, 1993.
48. Wally Hammond.
49. Steve Waugh, 416 runs, av 83.20.

50. Derek Randall 174.
51. Tim Robinson.
52. Graeme Wood 172 and Greg Ritchie 146.
53. Bobby Simpson and Ken Barrington.
54. Eddie Hemmings.
55. Perth in 1978–79 when he made 102.
56. Chris Broad – 162 in Perth, 116 at Adelaide, 112 at Melbourne.

57. W R Hammond 905 in 1928–29; D C S Compton 753 in 1948; H Sutcliffe 734 in 1924–5; and D I Gower 732 in 1985.
58. Don Bradman 5028, Jack Hobbs 3636, Allan Border 3548 and David Gower 3269.
59. Don Bradman 974 in 1930, 810 in 1936–37, and Mark Taylor 839 in 1989.
60. 393 by Steve Waugh in 1989.
61. 1926.
62. Harry Graham, 107 in 1893.
63. David Steele of Northamptonshire.

64. Arthur Mailey 36 in 1920–21, two more than Shane Warne took in 1994.
65. Eric Hollies.
66. Richard Ellison.
67. R A L 'Bob' Massie 16–137 (8–84, 8–53). This was his first appearance in Australia v England Tests.
68. Terry Alderman.
69. Shane Warne of Australia at Manchester in 1993.
70. 5–61 v Australia at Sydney in 1990–91.

71. Craig McDermott.
72. Rodney Hogg.
73. Geoff Lawson.
74. Dennis Lillee 167 in 29 Tests at an average of 21.00.
75. Hedley Verity.
76. Bob Willis.
77. Devon Malcolm.

78. Terry Alderman, 42 for Australia in England in 1981 and 41 for Australia in England in 1989.
79. Tom Veivers.
80. L O B Fleetwood Smith 87–11–298–1 for Australia v England at The Oval in 1938.
81. Terry Alderman, 6–47.
82. John Snow.
83. Dennis Lillie and Terry Alderman – 11.
84. W J 'Bill' O'Reilly.

Wicketkeeping and Fielding

85. Alec Stewart
86. Jack Russell in Melbourne, 1990–91.
87. Godfrey Evans 91, and Alan Knott 95.
88. Alan Knott – 105
89. Rodney Marsh off Dennis Lillee.
90. Allan Border.
91. Alan Knott 24 (21c, 3 st) v Australia in 1970–71.

92. R C 'Jack' Russell, 128 not out.
93. Rodney Marsh – six at Brisbane in 1982–83.
94. Ian Healy 26 (c 21 st 5) of Australia on the 1993 Tour.
95. C J 'Jack' Richards of Surrey.
96. Geoff Miller.
97. Jack Gregory, 15 for Australia v England in 1920–21.
98. Rodney Marsh, 28 for Australia v England in 1982–83.

99. Roger Tolchard of Leicestershire.
100. England v Australia in Brisbane, 1982–83.
101. W Storer.
102. R W Taylor, England v India at Bombay in 1979–80, taking ten.
103. Terry Alderman.
104. S A R Silva for Sri Lanka v India in 1985–86.
105. v New Zealand at Lord's, 1986 (Bruce French who was injured, Bill Athey, Bob Taylor and Bobby Parks).

Captains

106. Lindsay Hassett.
107. Ray Illingworth 1970–71 and Mike Brearley 1977–78/79, who both had seven.
108. 1982 v Pakistan at Lord's.
109. Mike Gatting, John Emburey, Chris Cowdrey, and Graham Gooch.
110. Peter van der Merwe in 1965.
111. Warwick Armstrong.
112. W G Grace who was 50 years 318 days at Nottingham in 1899.

113. Mike Atherton in 1993.
114. Mike Denness, 188 in 1974–75.
115. Allan Lamb.
116. Graham Gooch, 3582, average 58.72 with 11 centuries in 34 Tests.
117. Mark Burgess.
118. Archie McLaren – 22.
119. David Gower v West Indies at Lord's.

120. Barry Jarman at Headingley in 1968.
121. Mike Atherton who reached his century in 424 minutes for England at Sydney in 1990–91.
122. Bobby Simpson, 311 in 608 minutes at Old Trafford, 1964. (This was also the slowest triple-century.)
123. W L 'Billy' Murdoch, 211 at The Oval, 1884; R B 'Bobby' Simpson, 311 at Old Trafford, 1964; A R 'Alan' Border, 200 not out at Headingley, 1993.
124. A C MacLaren, 109 v Australia at Sydney in 1897–98; Allan Lamb, 119 v West Indies at Bridgetown in 1989–90.
125. Ian Botham and Greg Chappell.
126. Geoffrey Boycott.

ANSWERS TO CHAPTER 2

Test Cricket Around The World

Australia

1. Mark Taylor.
2. Kim Hughes.
3. Rodney Marsh, 355.
4. W M 'Bill' Woodfull.
5. Allan Border.
6. Doug Walters – 6.
7. Dean Jones, 102.

8. Steve Waugh.
9. Damien Fleming for Australia v Pakistan at Rawalpindi in 1994–95.
10. Neil Harvey.
11. Allan Border, 7–46 and 4–50.
12. Mark Waugh v Sri Lanka facing a total of 12 balls in the 2nd and 3rd Test matches.
13. J M Gregory, 70 minutes, Australia v South Africa at Johannesburg, 1921–22.
14. Alan Davidson, 5–135, 6–87.

15. Lindsay Kline at Cape Town.
16. Bill Ponsford and Doug Walters.
17. Archie Jackson.
18. Charlie Macartney v England at Leeds in 1926, and Stan McCabe v South Africa at Johannesburg in 1935.
19. Jimmy Matthews.
20. Mark Taylor v West Indies at Adelaide in 1988–89.
21. Bill Brown of Australia by Vinoo Mankad of India in 1947–48.

22. Curtly Elconn Lynwall Ambrose of West Indies.
23. Richie Richardson (eight).
24. Richie Richardson.
25. Alvin Kallicharran.
26. India.
27. Sunil Gavaskar of India (thirteen).
28. Clive Lloyd – 74.

29. Malcolm Marshall, 376.
30. Courtney Walsh at Brisbane.
31. Gordon Greenidge.
32. Viv Richards.
33. Brian Lara, 277 v Australia at Sydney in 1992–93.
34. Collie Smith.
35. Jeff Stollmeyer.

36. Gordon Greenidge.
37. Joe Solomon, West Indies v Australia.
38. Oscar Hylton who toured England in 1939.
39. George Headley – Panama.
40. Jack Noreiga for West Indies v India at Port of Spain, Trinidad, in 1970–71.
41. George Headley for West Indies in 1939, who scored 106 and 107.
42. Lawrence Rowe and Alvin Kallicharran both v New Zealand in 1971–72. Rowe is the only batsman to do so in his first match.

43. Imran Khan, 362.
44. Aqib Javed.
45. Younis Ahmed of Pakistan, between 1969 and 1987.
46. Imran Khan, 40 wickets v India in 1982–83.
47. Mohsin Khan 200 in 1982.
48. Salim Malik.
49. Imran Khan 117 and 6–98 and 5–82 v India at Faisalabad in 1982–83.

50. Hanif, Wazir, Mushtaq, and Sadiq Mohammad.
51. Zaheer Abbas.
52. Hanif Mohammad, whose 337 took 16 hours 10 minutes for Pakistan v West Indies at Bridgetown, 1957–58.
53. Wasim Akram.
54. v India at Karachi in 1989–90.
55. 7–79 for Pakistan v New Zealand at Faisalabad in 1990–91.
56. Mushtaq Mohammad, aged 17 and 82 days, scored 101 for Pakistan v India at Delhi in 1960–61.

57. Mohsin Khan.
58. Javed Miandad.
59. Hanif and Shoaib Mohammad.
60. Khan Mohammad for Pakistan v West Indies at Kingston in 1957–58, 54–5–259–0.
61. Asif Iqbal and Intikhab Alam at The Oval in 1967.
62. Abdul Qadir.
63. Australia 80 all out, Pakistan 15–2 in October 1956 – a playing day of 5.5 hours.

64. Nawab of Pataudi Senior and Junior in 1946 and 1967 respectively.
65. Nawab of Pataudi Jnr for India v West Indies in 1961–62.
66. Vinod Kambli.
67. Kapil Dev.
68. Sachin Tendulkar, 59, India v Pakistan at Faisalabad, aged 16.
69. Mohinder Amarnath of India.
70. Mohammed Azharuddin – 6.

71. H P Tillekaratne of Sri Lanka at Ahmedabad in 1994.
72. Sunil Gavaskar, three times.
73. Vinod Kambli, 227 for India v Zimbabwe in Delhi; 224 for India v England in Bombay.
74. Sunil Gavaskar 774 for India v West Indies 1970–71.
75. 406–4 by India v West Indies at Port of Spain, 1975–76.
76. N D Hirwani.
77. Sunil Gavaskar of India, 34.

78. Sadiq Mohammad of Pakistan at Faisalabad in 1978.
79. Chetan Chauhan who scored 2,084.
80. Sanjay Manjrekar, 218 at Lahore in 1989–90.
81. Maharajah of Porbander.
82. Maninder Singh.
83. Sunil Gavaskar, 127 not out in a total of 286 for India v Pakistan in 1982–83 at Faisalabad.
84. K S More for India v West Indies at Madras in 1987–88.

New Zealand

85. Ken Rutherford.
86. Tom Lowry.
87. Sanjay Manjrekar of India v New Zealand at Christchurch in 1989–90.
88. Chris Pringle.
89. Richard Hadlee on 36 occasions.
90. Martin Crowe (five).
91. Martin Crowe at Wellington in 1990–91.

92. Gavin Larsen of New Zealand, 53 appearances in one-day internationals. He was also the New Zealand vice-captain in England in 1994 and appeared in his first Test match at Nottingham v England in 1994.
93. 467 by Andrew Jones and Martin Crowe for New Zealand v Sri Lanka at Wellington in 1990–91.
94. John Wright.
95. Ian Smith.
96. R C 'Dick' Motz who took 100 in 32 Tests.
97. Richard Hadlee 9–52 v Australia at Brisbane in 1985–86.
98. Richard Hadlee, 15–124 v Australia at Brisbane in 1985–86.

99. Peter Petherick for New Zealand v Pakistan at Lahore in 1976–77.
100. 223 not out by Glenn Turner for New Zealand v West Indies at Kingston in 1971–72.
101. Dunedin, New Zealand v Pakistan in 1988–89.
102. Dayle and Richard Hadlee; Geoff and Hedley Howarth; John and Nicholas (N M) Parker; and Jeff and Martin Crowe.
103. Giff and Graham Vivian; Walter, Dayle and Richard Hadlee; Mac and Robert Anderson; Lance and Chris Cairns; Wynne and Grant Bradburn; and P G Z 'Zin' and Chris Harris.
104. John Bracewell, 1001 runs and 102 wickets in 41 Tests.
105. John Wright, Martin Crowe, Bev Congdon, John Reid and Richard Hadlee.

106. Ali Bacher.
107. 1935 at Lord's.
108. 274 by Graeme Pollock at Kingsmead, Durban, 1969–70.
109. Trevor Goddard.
110. Allan Donald, 5–55 and 7–84.
111. Bruce Mitchell, 3,471.
112. Brian McMillan.

113. Hugh Tayfield (an off-spinner) who completed the century by dismissing Tom Graveney at The Oval in 1955.
114. Graham Pollock, 122 v Australia at Sydney in 1963–64.
115. S J Cook v West Indies at Bridgetown 1991–92.
116. Andrew 'A C' Hudson, 163 at Bridgetown, Barbados.
117. Omar Henry v India at Durban in 1992.
118. Denis Lindsay in 1966–67.
119. Trevor Goddard at Johannesburg in 1964–65.

120. Hugh Tayfield, 9–113 (13–192 in the match) for South Africa v England at Johannesburg (4th Test) in 1956–57.
121. A B Tancred, 26 not out of 47 all out for South Africa v England at Cape Town in 1888–89.
122. A J 'Tony' Traicos who, aged 45 at the time of this Test, had previously played for South Africa v Australia in 1969–70; 22 years 222 days had elapsed, therefore, since he had previously played Test cricket – a record gap between Test appearances.
123. Andrew Hudson v West Indies at Bridgetown, 1991–92.
124. Aubrey Faulkner.
125. Lee Irvine (v Australia), 102 at Port Elizabeth.
126. A W 'Dave' Nourse in 1922–23.

Answers to Chapter 3

County Cricket

Batting

1. Essex 134 at Chelmsford.
2. 228 for Leicestershire v Glamorgan at Leicester in 1989.
3. Graeme Hick, 57.10 at the end of the 1994 season for a total of 22,901 runs.
4. Graeme Hick and Mike Gatting.
5. Graeme Hick.
6. Roger Twose, 277 not out for Warwickshire v Glamorgan at Edgbaston.
7. Phil Simmons for Leicestershire v Northamptonshire at Leicester scored 261 and beat Sam Coe's 252 not out achieved v Northants at Leicester in 1914, the Leicestershire individual highest score.

8. Javed Miandad.
9. 102 not out v Middlesex at Lord's in 1976.
10. Lancashire at Blackpool in 1975.
11. Graham Gooch 12, and Hugh Morris 10.
12. Neil Fairbrother, 366 for Lancashire v Surrey in 1990, and it beat Len Hutton's 364 for England v Australia in 1938.
13. Graeme Hick of Worcestershire in 1986, aged 20.
14. John Langridge of Sussex.

15. Frank Woolley.
16. C P 'Philip' Mead, 48,892 av 48.84, between 1905 and 1936.
17. Les Berry, 45 between 1924–51.

18. Glenn Turner, 83.4% (141 out of 169) for Worcestershire v Glamorgan in 1977.
19. Colin Cowdrey and Dennis Amiss – 9.
20. E B 'Ted' Alletson of Nottinghamshire.
21. Bert Sutcliffe, 385 for Otago v Canterbury at Christchurch in 1952–53.

Bowling

22. Somerset in 1991.
23. Worcestershire.
24. Courtney Walsh.
25. Steve Watkin of Glamorgan – 92.
26. Leicestershire and Hampshire.
27. Wilfred Rhodes – 4,187.
28. Hedley Verity 10–10 v Nottinghamshire at Leeds in 1932.

29. A P 'Tich' Freeman of Kent.
30. 7–14 for Essex v Worcestershire at Ilford in 1982.
31. Martin McCague of Kent.
32. Les Jackson.
33. John Emburey.
34. Don Shepherd.
35. Brad Donelan.

36. Dexter Fitton of Lancashire, an off-spinner.
37. Mark Robinson of Yorkshire, then of Northamptonshire.
38. 1993, Gloucestershire v Sussex at Hove.
39. N I 'Ian' Thomson, 10–49 for Sussex v Warwickshire at Worthing in 1964.
40. Derek Shackleton of Hampshire.
41. G C Harrison, an off-spinner playing for Ireland v Scotland in Edinburgh, who took 9–113.
42. P S Gerrans of Oxford University v Lancashire at Oxford.

All-rounders

43. Mike Watkinson.
44. John Emburey of Middlesex.
45. Jimmy Adams.
46. Frank Woolley.
47. Mike Watkinson of Lancashire.
48. Manoj Prabhakar.
49. Malcolm Nash of Glamorgan at Swansea – Sobers was playing for Nottinghamshire.

50. Ray Illingworth.
51. J H Parks, 3,003 runs and 101 wickets in 1937.
52. Kevin Curran.
53. Wilfred Rhodes – 16.
54. Eddie Barlow.
55. Richard Hadlee in 1984 and Franklyn Stephenson in 1988.
56. Ken MacLeay.

57. Mike Procter for Gloucestershire v Essex at Westcliff in 1972 and for Gloucestershire v Leicestershire at Bristol in 1979.
58. Johnnie J W H T Douglas and Derek Pringle, both of whom went to Felsted.
59. Arthur Milton – cricket for Gloucestershire and football for Arsenal.
60. George Hirst 2,385 runs and 208 wickets.
61. B J T Bosanquet for Middlesex v Sussex at Lord's 103, 100 not out, 3–75 and 8–53 in 1905; F D Stephenson for Nottinghamshire v Yorkshire at Nottingham 111, 117, 4–105 and 7–117 in 1988.
62. George Hirst, Raymond Illingworth and Wilfred Rhodes.
63. Alan Rees of Glamorgan v Middlesex at Lord's in 1965.

Overseas players

64. Dean Jones of Australia.
65. Sachin Tendulkar in 1992.
66. David Boon.
67. Anderson Cummins of West Indies.
68. Somerset.
69. Derbyshire.
70. Lance Gibbs, Alvin Kallicharran, Rohan Kanhai, and Deryck Murray.

71. Michael Bevan of New South Wales and Australia.
72. Jimmy Cook of Somerset.
73. J E 'Joey' Benjamin of Surrey; W K M 'Winston' Benjamin of Leicestershire (now Hampshire); K C G 'Kenneth' Benjamin of Worcestershire.
74. Alvin Kallicharran, playing for Warwickshire v Lancashire at Southport in 1982.
75. 322, for Somerset v Warwickshire at Taunton in 1985.
76. Barry Richards of Hampshire.
77. W E 'Bill' Alley.

78. Maurice Tate, 1,193 runs and 116 wickets.
79. Albert Trott.
80. S J 'Jimmy' Cook, 313 not out, Somerset v Glamorgan at Cardiff in 1990.
81. Tom Moody in 1990.
82. Graham Gooch.
83. Vincent van de Bijl of Middlesex.
84. Lancashire.

85. Paul Farbrace and Graham Kersey.
86. Ian Gould.
87. Chris Scott.
88. John Carr of Middlesex – 41 in 1992, 39 in 1993.
89. Jimmy Binks of Yorkshire between 1955 and 1969.
90. Richard Blakey of Yorkshire in 1987.
91. Jack Russell in 1989.

92. Jack Russell for Gloucestershire v Surrey at The Oval in 1986 (taken off successive balls from Courtney Walsh and David 'Syd' Lawrence).
93. Graham Gooch.
94. Godfrey Evans.
95. Les Ames – 2482 runs and 104 dismissals in 1932.
96. Frank Woolley 1018 between 1906–1938.
97. Walter Hammond – 78 in 1928.
98. Steve Marsh of Kent v Middlesex at Lord's.

99. Bob Taylor, 1649 between 1960 and 1988.
100. Leslie Ames, 128 in 1929, 122 in 1928, and 104 in 1932.
101. Micky Stewart of Surrey v Northamptonshire at Northampton, and A S 'Tony' Brown of Gloucestershire v Nottinghamshire at Nottingham in 1966.
102. Paul Nixon of Leicestershire.
103. W H Brain off C L Townsend for Gloucestershire v Somerset at Cheltenham in 1893.
104. Chris Tavaré of Kent in 1978 (he took 49).
105. Les Ames (3 times) and John Murray (once).

106. Phil Bainbridge.
107. Ian Botham, Viv Richards, and Joel Garner.
108. Essex.
109. Tony Wright.
110. Keith Fletcher.
111. Richard Stemp.
112. 1984.

113. Norman Cowans, who first played for England in 1979–80 and was not capped until 1984.
114. Bill Athey, Eddie Hemmings, and David Smith.
115. Norman Cowans, formerly of Middlesex; and Kevin Shine, formerly of Hampshire.
116. Arnie Sidebottom.
117. Trevor Bailey in 1959.
118. Kent v Worcestershire at Tunbridge Wells in 1960.
119. H F T 'Bertie' Buse of Somerset v Lancashire at Bath in 1953.

120. Allan Jones, now a first-class umpire: Sussex 1966–69, Somerset 1970–75, Middlesex 1976–79, Glamorgan 1980–81.
121. Sussex v Kent at Home in 1991; Sussex scoring 436, the highest total to tie a first-class match.
122. Sussex v Essex at Hove in 1993, 1808 for 20 wickets.
123. Lancashire beat Leicestershire at Old Trafford in 1956 by 10 wickets. Their opening batsmen were Alan Wharton and 'Jack' Dyson.
124. Derek Randall for Nottinghamshire v Derbyshire at Trent Bridge, when a different pitch was cut after the first was deemed unsuitable.
125. Wilfred Rhodes of Yorkshire, 763 between 1898 and 1930; and Frank Woolley of Kent, 707 between 1906 and 1938.
126. Ken Suttle of Sussex, 423 between 1954 and 1969.

ANSWERS TO CHAPTER 4

One-day Cricket

Internationals

1. Darren Gough of Yorkshire and Shaun Udal of Hampshire.
2. 363–7 (55 overs) by England v Pakistan at Nottingham in 1992.
3. Robin Smith, 167 not out v Australia at Birmingham in 1993.
4. Aqib Javed.
5. Allan Border – 273.
6. Jeff Dujon – 204.
7. Mark Greatbatch, 102 not out and 111 v England in 1990.

8. Australia and England at Melbourne in 1970–71; Australia won by 5 wickets.
9. Kapil Dev of India who dismissed R S Mahanama, S T Jayasuriya and R J Ratnayake.
10. Viv Richards, 189 not out for West Indies v England at Old Trafford, Manchester, in 1984.
11. Desmond Haynes of West Indies.
12. Kapil Dev of India.
13. 43 (19.5 overs) by Pakistan v West Indies at Cape Town in 1992–93.
14. Desmond Haynes – 16.

15. Jeff Wilson.
16. Monte Lynch.

17. 5–20 by Vic Marks v New Zealand, Wellington, 1983–84.
18. Geoff Marsh – 9.
19. Mark Lathwell.
20. One – Ian Botham.
21. Jim Love.

22. Asif Din of Warwickshire.
23. Dermot Reeve for Sussex in 1986 and Warwickshire in 1989.
24. 1991 v Surrey.
25. Geoff Boycott, 146 for Yorkshire v Surrey in 1965.
26. Alvin Kallicharran, 206 for Warwickshire v Oxfordshire at Birmingham in 1984.
27. Graham Gooch (nine).
28. Tom Moody of Worcestershire.

29. Graham Rose off 36 balls, for Somerset v Devon at Torquay in 1990.
30. Lancashire.
31. Geoff Arnold of Surrey, 81, between 1963 and 1980.
32.. Ted Dexter v Worcestershire in 1963 and Warwickshire in 1964.
33. David Smith of Sussex 124, and Asif Din of Warwickshire 104, in the 1993 Final between Sussex and Warwickshire.
34. Hertfordshire, in 1976.
35. Chris Smith of Hampshire (seven).

36. Michael Holding, 8–21 for Derbyshire v Sussex at Hove in 1988.
37. Durham, who beat Yorkshire by 5 wickets at Harrogate in 1973.
38. Tim Curtis and Tom Moody, an unbroken stand of 308 for the third wicket for Worcestershire v Surrey at The Oval in 1994.
39. David Sydenham for Surrey v Cheshire at Hoylake in 1964.
40. Phillip DeFreitas of Lancashire.
41. Graham Gooch – 2383 at an average of 52.92 for Essex between 1973 and 1994.
42. Asif Din in 103 balls for Warwickshire v Sussex in 1993.

43. Warwickshire and Worcestershire.
44. Derbyshire, who beat Lancashire.
45. Paul Smith of Warwickshire, who took 3–34 and made 42 not out.
46. Durham, Glamorgan, and Sussex.
47. John Abrahams of Lancashire, who beat Warwickshire in the Final.
48. Worcestershire.
49. Lancashire v Hampshire at Old Trafford in 1990.

50. Leicestershire.
51. Kent in 1973, 1976 and 1978, and Leicestershire in 1972, 1975 and 1985 – both 3 times.
52. Kent, who lost to Warwickshire at Edgbaston after rain had prevented play on both days.
53. Dominic Cork.
54. 50 by Hampshire v Yorkshire at Leeds in 1991.
55. 290–6 by Essex v Surrey in 1979.
56. 285 unbroken for the second wicket by Gordon Greenidge and David Turner for Hampshire v Minor Counties South at Amersham in 1973.

57. Derek Taylor of Somerset v Combined Universities.
58. Brian Rose of Somerset.
59. Eddie Hemmings of Nottinghamshire.
60. Ken Higgs for Leicestershire v Surrey at Lord's in 1974.
61. Graham Gooch, 120 for Essex v Surrey in 1979; and Viv Richards, 132 not out for Somerset v Surrey in 1981.
62. Joel Garner, 5–14 for Somerset v Surrey in 1981; and Stephen Jefferies, 5–13 for Hampshire v Derbyshire in 1988.
63. 7–12, Wayne Daniel for Middlesex v Minor Counties East at Ipswich in 1978.

Sunday League

64. Carl Hooper.
65. Warwickshire.
66. 23 by Middlesex v Yorkshire at Leeds in 1974.
67. Viv Richards 26 for Somerset in 1977.
68. 8–0–96–1 by Dominic Cork for Derbyshire v
    Nottinghamshire at Nottingham in 1993.
69. Glamorgan.
70. 375–4 by Surrey v Yorkshire at Scarborough in 1994.

71. 8–26 by Keith Boyce for Essex v Lancashire, Manchester,
    1971.
72. 176 by Graham Gooch for Essex v Glamorgan at Southend
    in 1983.
73. 1992.
74. Wayne Larkins – 12.
75. John Lever of Essex – 386.
76. Essex.
77. Tom Moody of Worcestershire in 1991.

78. Graham Gooch.
79. Viv Richards – 26 in 1977.
80. 273 for the second wicket by Graham Gooch and Ken
    McEwan for Essex v Nottinghamshire at Nottingham in
    1983.
81. Brian Langford for Somerset v Essex at Yeovil in 1969.
82. Bob Clapp of Somerset in 1974, and Clive Rice of
    Nottinghamshire in 1986; they both took 34.
83. David Bairstow of Yorkshire.
84. Keith Boyce 8–26, Richard Hutton 7–15, Tony Hodgson
    7–39 and Adrian Jones 7–41.

85. Kerry Packer.
86. Tony Greig.
87. Curtley Ambrose.
88. Gary Kirsten 112 not out v Australia at Melbourne.
89. Allan Border at Sydney.
90. 158 v New Zealand at Brisbane in 1982–83.
91. Allan Border, who achieved the milestone in a WSC match for Australia v Pakistan at Sydney in 1989–90.

92. Allan Border and Imran Khan Australia v Pakistan in a WSC match at Melbourne in 1989–90.
93. David Gower 122, 158 and 109 v New Zealand.
94. Dean Jones.
95. 1986–87 – Mike Gatting.
96. David Boon and Geoff Marsh.
97. Dean Jones 145 v England at Brisbane.
98. Mark Taylor of Australia.

99. Trevor Chappell by Greg Chappell for Australia v New Zealand at Melbourne.
100. Brian McKechnie who needed to hit a six off the last ball to win the match.
101. Simon O'Donnell, Australia v Pakistan.
102. Glenn McGrath, Australia v South Africa at Melbourne.
103. 603, Pakistan v Sri Lanka at Adelaide in 1989–90.
104. Phil Simmons (the most economical figures ever recorded from a full bowling stint).
105. 202, Ramiz Raja and Saeed Anwar for Pakistan v Sri Lanka in 1989–90.

106. Pakistan who beat England in the Final.
107. Australia, who beat England.
108. India, Pakistan and Sri Lanka.
109. Graham Gooch.
110. Winston Davis, 7–51 for West Indies v Australia at Leeds in 1975.
111. Viv Richards for West Indies v England.
112. David Gower, 384.

113. Kapil Dev's 175 not out for India v Zimbabwe at Tunbridge Wells in 1983.
114. David Boon of Australia.
115. Martin Snedden, New Zealand v England at The Oval in 1983; 12–1–105–2.
116. Bishen Bedi, 12–8–6–1 for India v East Africa at Leeds in 1975.
117. Sunil Gavaskar of India.
118. Craig McDermott, who took 5–44.
119. Reliance Industries.

120. Mohinder Amarnath.
121. Clive Lloyd, 102 for West Indies v Australia in 1975 at Lord's.
122. Gary Gilmour of Australia.
123. 126 unbroken by Kapil Dev and Syed Kirmani for India v Zimbabwe in 1975 at Tunbridge Wells.
124. Gary Gilmour of Australia 5–48.
125. Duncan Fletcher.
126. Roger Binny, 18 at 18.67 runs per wicket.

ANSWERS TO CHAPTER 5

Cricket Grounds

England

1. Angus Fraser, who took 8–131 in the match.
2. The Oval in 1880.
3. 333 by Graham Gooch for England v India in 1990.
4. 278 by Denis Compton v Pakistan in 1954.
5. Craig White and Stephen Rhodes.
6. Dion Nash, New Zealand v England, 1994; 56 and 6–76, and 5–93 (11–169).
7. Martin Donnelly, 206 in 1949.

8. 1934.
9. Headingley 1975.
10. Tim May.
11. Willie Watson and Trevor Bailey.
12. Kim Hughes of Australia.
13. Chris Tavaré.
14. Allan Lamb.

15. Ian Healy, 102 not out.
16. Jimmy Burke.
17. 1935.
18. 4th Test match at Old Trafford in 1989.
19. Graham Gooch, David Gower, and Geoff Boycott.
20. Geoff Pullar, 131 v India in 1959. Mike Atherton also scored 131 v India in 1990.
21. N D Hirwani.

West Indies

22. Bridgetown for Barbados v Trinidad.
23. Robin Jackman.
24. Bourda, Georgetown, Guyana.
25. Kensington Oval, Bridgetown, Barbados.
26. Recreation Ground, St John's, Antigua.
27. Kensington Oval, Bridgetown, Barbados – named after Frank Worrell, Everton Weekes and Clyde Walcott.
28. 365 not out by Gary Sobers v Pakistan 1957–58.

29. Viv Richards, 56 balls, West Indies v England, at St John's, Antigua, in 1985–86.
30. Curtly Ambrose.
31. Sunil Gavaskar.
32. Sabina Park, Kingston, Jamaica.
33. Tony Greig, 8–86 and 5–70 at Port of Spain.
34. Sunil Gavaskar.
35. Colin Croft, 8–29.

36. Andrew Sandham, 325, England v West Indies at Sabina Park, Jamaica in 1929–30.
37. Devon Malcolm, 10–137, 4–60 and 6–77.
38. Bourda, Georgetown, Guyana.
39. Ian Johnson for Australia v West Indies 7–44 in 1954–55.
40. Pickwick Cricket Club.
41. Peter Willey, 102 for England in 1980–81.
42. Kensington Oval, Bridgetown.

43. Woolloongabba, Brisbane, Australia.
44. 12.
45. Melbourne.
46. 1970–71 at Melbourne.
47. Sydney Cricket Ground.
48. Adelaide Oval.
49. Sydney in 1903–04.

50. 45 v Australia at Sydney in 1886–87.
51. Gary Sobers 132, and Norman O'Neill 181.
52. Melbourne – W H Ponsford 437 and 429.
53. 452 not out by Don Bradman for NSW v Queensland in 1929–30.
54. Bob Willis.
55. Perth by Merv Hughes for Australia v West Indies in 1988–89.
56. Brisbane in 1946–47 by an innings and 332 runs.

57. 675 runs, Brisbane at the Exhibition Ground.
58. The Oval in 1909 when he scored 136 and 130.
59. v Australia at Melbourne in 1907–08.
60. Dean Jones, 116 and 121 not out.
61. Bobby Simpson, 225 in 1965–66.
62. Patsy Hendren, 169 in 1928–29.
63. Keith Stackpole, 207 in 1970–71.

64. Braboume Stadium.
65. Dacca Stadium, Dacca.
66. Madras, India.
67. Calcutta.
68. Delhi.
69. Kanpur.
70. Niaz Stadium, Hyderabad.

71. Karachi.
72. Calcutta.
73. Ahmadabad.
74. Lala Amarnath, 118 v England on the Gymkhana Ground, Bombay in 1933–34.
75. Wankhede Stadium, Bombay v England in the Golden Jubilee Test of 1979–80.
76. Chepauk, Madras 236 not out v West Indies in 1983–84.
77. Abdul Qadir.

78. National Stadium, Karachi – The President was Dwight D Eisenhower Pakistan v Australia in December 1959.
79. 44 and 5 v Pakistan at Lahore in 1990–91.
80. Baroda in 1946–47, V S Hazare and Gul Mahomed.
81. The P Saravanamuttu Stadium Ground, Colombo in 1982. Three further grounds in Colombo have since been used for Test matches.
82. Poona, 2,376 for 37 wickets, Maharashtra v Bombay in 1948–49.
83. Nagpur for India v New Zealand at Nagpur in 1987.
84. Calcutta v West Indies in 1978–79.

New Zealand

85. Lord's, 551–9 declared in 1973.
86. Lancaster Park, Christchurch in 1930.
87. Bevan Congdan 175, Mark Burgess 105 and Vic Pollard 105 not out.
88. Eden Park, Auckland.
89. Lancaster Park, Christchurch v England in 1930.
90. Eden Park, Auckland.
91 Carisbrook, Dunedin.

92. Phil Tufnell.
93. Napier.
94. Basin Reserve, Wellington.
95. Eden Park, Auckland v West Indies.
96. Lancaster Park, Christchurch.
97. Carisbrook, Dunedin.
98. Rodney Redmond.

99. M J C 'Maurie' Allom.
100. Christchurch.
101. New Plymouth Sri Lanka v Zimbabwe.
102. Hamilton in 1990–91.
103. Lancaster Park, Christchurch.
104. Wellington, Basin Reserve.
105. Hagley Park.

106. Kingsmead, Durban, 622–9 declared v Australia in 1969–70.
107. Durban.
108. Harare Sports Club, Harare v India in 1992.
109. Kingsmead, Durban.
110. Graeme Pollock, 274 v Australia.
111. Hugh Tayfield, 9–113; he also caught the 10th wicket.
112. St George's Park, Port Elizabeth.

113. Benoni in North East Transvaal in 1948–49.
114. Neil Harvey.
115. St. George's Park, Port Elizabeth.
116. Durban.
117. Newlands, Cape Town.
118. George Lohmann.
119. Jimmy Sinclair 106 v England.

120. Roy McLean in 1955.
121. Allan Lamb, 294.
122. St George's Park, Port Elizabeth.
123. It is now the site of Johannesburg Railway Station.
124. East London, where Border totalled 16 and 18 v Natal in 1959–60.
125. Newlands, Cape Town.
126. A C 'Jack' Russell of England.

ANSWERS TO CHAPTER 6

Cricket Records

England v Australia

1. David Boon, 555 at 69.37.
2. Graham Gooch, 673 at 56.08.
3. Peter Such, 16 at 33.81.
4. Steve Waugh.
5. David Boon.
6. Don Bradman at Headingley in 1930.
7. 1989 – Mark Taylor 839, Dean Jones 566, and Steve Waugh 506.

8. 30 in the five Tests of 1921.
9. Manchester 1896 and 1938, and Melbourne 1970–71.
10. 18 between Melbourne in 1986–87 and The Oval in 1993.
11. Neil Foster of Essex.
12. Rodney Marsh – 42.
13. Three – 1948, Don Bradman's side; 1989 and 1993, Allan Border's sides.
14. Robin Smith – 553, av 61.44.

15. Carl Rackemann.
16. W G Grace, 152 at The Oval v Australia in 1880.
17. Harry Makepeace for England v Australia at Melbourne in 1920–21, aged 40.
18. J J Ferris; W E Midwinter; W E Murdoch; A E Trott; and S M J Woods.
19. Clem Hill, 98 and 97 at Adelaide in 1901–02; and Frank Woolley, 95 and 93 at Lord's in 1921.
20. 382 by Bill Lawry and Bobby Simpson.
21. Jack Hobbs, 3,636 runs and 12 centuries.

22. Charlie Macartney.
23. Mike Brearley.
24. Colin Cowdrey.
25. Barry Richards, 356 for South Africa v Western Australia at Perth.
26. R M 'Bob' Cowper.
27. W G Grace in 1876, 318 not out for Gloucestershire v Yorkshire at Cheltenham.
28. Hanif Mohammed for Pakistan v West Indies at Bridgetown in 1957–58; 16 hours 10 mins.

29. F R 'Frank' Foster, 305 not out for Warwickshire v Worcestershire at Dudley in 1914.
30. Graeme Hick, 405 not out for Worcestershire v Somerset at Taunton.
31. Glenn Turner.
32. Everton Weekes of West Indies.
33. Jack Robertson, 331 not out v Worcestershire at Worcester in 1949.
34. W H 'Bill' Ponsford.
35. R H 'Dick' Moore, 316 for Hampshire v Warwickshire at at Bournemouth; and Eddie Paynter, 322 for Lancashire v Sussex at Hove in 1937.

36. M V Sridhar, 366 for Hyderabad v Andhra at Secunderabad in January 1994.
37. Daryll Cullinan, 337 for Transvaal v Northern Transvaal in 1992–93.
38. Ken Rutherford, 317 for New Zealanders v D B Close's XI.
39. Geoff Marsh.
40. B B Nimbalkar, 443 not out for Maharashtra v Kathiawar at Poona in 1948–49.
41. W V Raman 313, and Arjan Kripal Singh 302 not out for Tamil Nadu v Goa at Panjim in 1988–89.
42. W W Keeton in 1939 since Lord's was required for the Eton v Harrow match.

43. A P 'Tich' Freeman of Kent in 1928 (304).
44. Ian Botham – 80 in 1985.
45. A E Arthur Fagg for Kent v Essex at Colchester in 1938.
46. Jason Gallian, who reached his century in 7 hrs 33 mins for Lancashire v Derbyshire at Stockport.
47. Denis Compton, 18 in 1947.
48. Pat Pocock of Surrey.
49. K S Ranjitsinhji who, in 1899, made 3,159 runs at 63.18 per innings.

50. Derbyshire.
51. Bruce French of Nottinghamshire.
52. John Carr of Middlesex, av 90.70.
53. M A 'Mark' Robinson.
54. Glenn Turner, 1,018 av 78.30 in 1973; Graeme Hick, 1,019 av 101.90 in 1988.
55. Brian Lara, 390 for Warwickshire v Durham in 1994.
56. Herbert Sutcliffe and Percy Holmes of Yorkshire.

57. 95.3% – Henry Enthoven, 102 not out of 107 with Fred Price for Middlesex v Sussex at Lord's in 1930.
58. 258, Hampshire v Derbyshire at Chesterfield – Chris Smith 114 and Kevan James 101. The other batsmen totalled 24 between them.
59. Derek Underwood of Kent in 1963 (aged 18 years).
60. Alan Jones of Glamorgan.
61. Pat Pocock for Surrey v Sussex at Eastbourne in 1972.
62. Albert Trott for Middlesex v Somerset at Lord's in 1907.
63. Javagal Srinath for Karnataka v Hyderabad in the Ranji Trophy, 1989–90.

64. 721, Australians v Essex at Southend in 1948.
65. David Boon.
66. Lancashire.
67. Matthew Hayden, who scored 1,150 runs.
68. 16 v MCC and at Lord's in 1896.
69. Kent.
70. Gary Kirsten 201 retired ill v Durham at Chester-le-Street.

71. Majid Khan. He later played county cricket for Glamorgan.
72. 613–8 declared v Sussex in 1994.
73. Warwick Armstrong and George Giffen.
74. Clive Lloyd for West Indies.
75. Graeme Hick, 187 for Worcestershire.
76. Victor Trumper 300 not out for Australians v Sussex at Hove in 1899.
77. Dean Jones.

78. Carl Hooper, 85.46 in 1991.
79. Mark Waugh 100 not out, and Steve Waugh 100 not out, for Essex v Australia at Chelmsford in 1993.
80. 278 for the Australians v MCC in 1938.
81. Tony Penberthy for Northamptonshire in 1989.
82. E J K Burn (he played in two Test matches).
83. Wayne Holdsworth.
84. George Giffen for Australians v Lancashire at Old Trafford; 13, 113 and 6–55, including a hat-trick in 1884.

85. Jack Hobbs – 197 between 1905 and 1934.
86. Graham Gooch, Allan Lamb and Mike Gatting.
87. Graeme Hick in 1990.
88. Doug Wright (seven).
89. Viv Richards – 114.
90. Denis Compton 3,816, and Bill Edrich 3,539, in 1947.
91. L E G 'Leslie' Ames.

92. C B Fry, Don Bradman, and Mike Procter.
93. 561 by Waheed Mirza and Mansoor Akhtar for Karachi Whites v Quetta at Karachi in 1976–77.
94. Don Bradman, av 115.66 in 1938; W A 'Bill' Johnston, av 102.00 in 1953; Geoffrey Boycott, av 100.12 in 1971 and av 102.53 in 1979; and Graham Gooch, av 101.70 in 1990.
95. Graham Gooch, to the end of the 1994 season.
96. A P 'Tich' Freeman of Kent in 1929, 1930, and 1931.
97. W G Grace (Gloucestershire) and Frank Woolley (Kent) – 28 times.
98. Ravi Shastri, Bombay v Baroda, Bombay, in 1984–85.

99. Hyderabad v Andhra at Secunderabad in January 1994; M V Sridar 366, V M Jaisimha 211, Noel David 207 not out. The innings totalled 944–6 wickets declared.
100. 260 by Amol Mazumdar for Bombay v Haryana at Faridabad in 1993–94.
101. Bob Crisp for Western Province v Griqualand West Johannesburg, 1931–32, and v Natal, Durban, 1933–34.
102. C B Fry, Don Bradman, Mike Procter, Ernest Tyldesley, Vijay Merchant, Wally Hammond, and Peter Kirsten.
103. 1,107 by Victoria v NSW at Melbourne in 1926–27.
104. Wilfred Rhodes, 4,187.

105. Zaheer Abbas, 216 not out and 150 not out v Surrey, The
     Oval, 1976; 230 not out and 104 not out v Kent,
     Canterbury, 1976; 205 not out and 108 not out v Sussex,
     Cheltenham, 1977; and 215 not out and 150 not out v
     Somerset, Bath, 1981.

Test records

106. Sunil Gavaskar 10,122; and Allan Border 11,174.
107. Jim Laker, 19 for England v Australia at Old Trafford in 1956.
108. Ken Barrington.
109. Kepler Wessels 104.
110. 99 at Lord's in 1994.
111. Don Bradman 117.
112. Don Bradman 974 runs in seven innings at an average of 139.14 v England in 1930.

113. Hugh Tayfield at Durban in 1956–57 v England.
114. Sonny Ramadhin of West Indies v England at Birmingham in 1978.
115. Richie Benaud of Australia.
116. Richard Illingworth for England v West Indies at Trent Bridge in 1991 when he dismissed Phil Simmons.
117. Mark Benson of Kent, John Stephenson of Essex, James Whitaker of Leicestershire, and Neil Williams of Middlesex.
118. Clem Hill – 96, 97, 98, 98 and 99.
119. Brian Lara, 277 at Sydney in 1992–93.

120. Five – Allan Border & Sunil Gavaskar (214), David Gower (204) and Desmond Haynes Graham Gooch (204).
121. Charlie Macartney, 112 v England at Headingley in 1926.
122. Don Bradman 12, Walter Hammond 7, and Javed Miandad 6.
123. Mudassar Nazar 231, and Javed Miandad 280 not out.
124. Miran Bux of Pakistan at the age of 47 years and 284 days v India in 1954–55.
125. Ian Botham, Colin Cowdrey, Walter Hammond and Graham Gooch.
126. James Southerton v Australia at Melbourne in 1877.

ANSWERS TO CHAPTER 7

Other Cricket

University and Schools cricket

1. Jason Gallian.
2. Russell Cake of Cambridge University – 108.
3. 1805.
4. John Crawley.
5. Andrew Ridley.
6. Graham Gooch for Essex.
7. Durham University.

8. C J 'Chris' Hollins, son of John Hollins.
9. Richard Yeabsley, 6–54 and 4–50.
10. Swansea, who beat Durham by 67 runs at Luton.
11. Mike Brearley, 4,310.
12. Derek Pringle in 1975.
13. Geoff Lovell.
14. Jason Gallian, Geoff Lovell and Richard Montgomerie.

15. Chinmay Gupte 122, and Chris Hollins 131.
16. Robin Boyd-Moss of Cambridge, 139 and 124.
17. 1827.
18. 238 not out by Nawab of Pataudi Senior for Oxford in 1931.
19. F C Cobden.
20. David Sheppard and John Dewes.
21. 1915.

22. Rapid Cricketline.
23. Staffordshire.
24. Devon who beat Lincolnshire by 18 runs.
25. New Zealand.
26. Jo Chamberlain.
27. Martin Moxon of Yorkshire.
28. Michael Vaughan of Yorkshire.

29. Durham v Yorkshire by 5 wickets at Harrogate in 1973.
30. Mark Nicholas of Hampshire.
31. John Crawley.
32. Mark Ilott, 37 wickets, av 13.92.
33. United Arab Emirates.
34. Karen Smithies, captain of the England women's team.
35. Zimbabwe.

36. Hertfordshire, in 1976.
37. Lincolnshire v Northumberland who won by 10 wickets: John Wileman (142 not out), lst innings Russell Evans; John Wileman (102 not out), 2nd innings Russell Evans.
38. Jack Potter of Victoria.
39. Richard Blakey.
40. Mark Ramprakash, 158 at Kandy (lst Test), and Nasser Hussain, 161 at Colombo (2nd Test).
41. Matthew Dowman, 267 at Hove in the second Test. He is now on Nottinghamshire's books. Shivnarnie Chanderpaul scored 203 not out in the first Test at Nottingham and played four Test matches in the winter for the West Indies.
42. Marcus Trescothick of Somerset 206.

Controversy

43. Headingley 1975.
44. Christ Broad at Sydney in 1987–88.
45. Imran Khan.
46. Graham Gooch.
47. John Morris (fellow Tiger Moth passenger) who scored 204 v Warwickshire in 1994.
48. Basil D'Oliveira.
49. Tony Greig prior to the series with West Indies.

50. Sarfaz Nawaz.
51. John Lever v India at New Delhi in 1976–77.
52. Geoff Griffins of South Africa v England at Lord's in 1960.
53. Robin Jackman in 1980–81.
54. Lancashire for their pitch v Middlesex at Old Trafford.
55. Headingley in 1972.
56. Sydney in 1970–71.

57. West Indies v Pakistan at Port of Spain, Trinidad, 1992–93.
58. Aqib Javed of Pakistan following an incident in the one-day international at Napier v New Zealand.
59. Brian Rose.
60. Essex (Southend), and Nottinghamshire (Trent Bridge).
61. 1935, when South Africa won their first Test match against England, in England.
62. Ian Foley.
63. Colin Croft.

64. Raymond Illingworth.
65. Peter May.
66. Don Wilson.
67. Dickie Bird.
68. Shakoor Rana.
69. Ken Palmer (it was his only Test match).
70. J B 'Brian' Bolus and F J 'Freddie' Titmus.

71. Steve Bucknor, England v New Zealand at Trent Bridge in 1994.
72. Trevor Jesty, capped by Hampshire, Surrey, and Lancashire.
73. Mike Turner.
74. Rodney Marsh.
75. David Richards, formerly of the Australian Cricket Board.
76. Lance Gibbs.
77. Graham Dilley, formerly of Kent.

78. Pakistan v India, 1989–90.
79. James Callaghan.
80. Phil Neale.
81. Tom Spencer 569 between 1950 and 1980.
82. Idris Begh.
83. John Lillywhite.
84. Sid Buller.

All-rounders

85. Graeme Hick with 315 runs, 8 wickets, and 5 catches.
86. Ian Botham at The Oval in 1991.
87. Ian Botham, 2113 runs and 145 wickets in 116 matches.
88. Simon O'Donnell and Steve Waugh.
89. Brian Close in 1949, aged 18.
90. Trevor Bailey, Fred Titmus and Ray Illingworth.
91. Five.

92. Ian Botham in 22 Tests achieved at Melbourne in 1982–83.
93. Bruce Dooland.
94. Ian Botham, 42 matches.
95. W G Grace, 54,896 runs and 2,876 wickets.
96. 'Gubby' Allen.
97. George Hurst, 208 wickets and 2,385 runs in 1906.
98. Jeffrey Dujon of West Indies and Rodney Marsh of Australia.

99. Warwick Armstrong and George Giffen – 30 times each.
100. Alan Davidson of Australia v West Indies, Brisbane 1960–61, 44 and 80, 5–135, and 6–87; Ian Botham of England v India, Bombay 1979–80, 114, 6–58 and 7–48; Imran Khan of Pakistan v India, Faisalabad 1982–83, 117, 6–98 and 5–82.
101. Ian Botham and Gary Sobers.
102. Ray Lindwall of Australia.
103. Jim Standen for West Ham United and Worcestershire.
104. Gubby Allen.
105. Albert Trott (twice) Alec Kennedy (one) and Maurice Tate (three times).

106. J P 'Jonathan' Agnew.
107. Derek Pringle of Essex.
108. Peter Roebuck.
109. Sir Neville Cardus.
110. John Nyren.
111. W H R 'Bill' Andrews.
112. C L R James.

113. E W 'Jim' Swanton.
114. Arthur Mailey who took 10–66 for the Australians v Gloucester at Cheltenham in 1921.
115. Don Bradman.
116. Matthew Engel.
117. Michael Manley.
118. R C Robertson, Glasgow.
119. Sir Pelham Warner.

120. Samuel Beckett, who twice in 1925 played for Dublin University against Northamptonshire.
121. *Pickwick Papers* by Charles Dickens. This match is also depicted on the current £10 English banknote.
122. Hirst and Spooner in *No Man's Land* by Harold Pinter.
123. James Pycroft.
124. A W Pullin.
125. Nicholas Wanostrocht, a schoolmaster and Kent cricketer in the days of Alfred Mynn and Fuller Pilch.
126. Jim Laker.

ANSWERS TO CHAPTER 8

General Knowledge/Trivia

Trivia 1

1. Mark Taylor.
2. Eight in 1988–89.
3. Liaqat Ali (Pakistan), Edgbaston, 1978.
4. In 1978 v Pakistan at Edgbaston.
5. Colin Bland, who ran out Ken Barrington and Jim Parks.
6. Cyril Washbrook, Denis Compton, and David Sheppard.
7. 117.

8. David Gower at Lord's v Australia in 1980.
9. Neil Fairbrother.
10. Graham Roope.
11. Graham Gooch.
12. Len Hutton, England v South Africa at The Oval in 1951.
13. George Lohmann who took 112 wickets at a rate of 34.12 balls per wicket. It is of interest to note that Waqar Younis, at the conclusion of the third Test against Zimbabwe in 1993–94, had taken 148 wickets at 36.22 balls per wicket, the second best in Test cricket history.
14. David Gower – 119 innings.

15. Norman Cowans v Australia at Perth in 1982–83.
16. Allan Border, 200 not out (4th Test) Headingley 1993.
17. Warren Bardsley for Australia v England at The Oval in 1909, 136 and 130.
18. Godfrey Evans, 97 mins for England v Australia, Adelaide 1946–47.

19. Darren Berry of South Australia achieved 2,447 in 1989–90.
20. Vinod Kambli and Sachin Tendulkar.
21. 307 by Alan Kippax and Hal Hooker for NSW v Victoria at Melbourne in 1928–29.

Trivia 2

22. Robin Smith.
23. 1929–30, v England and West Indies.
24. Donald Bradman, 37.
25. Sir Jack Hobbs in 1953.
26. Hastings Central Ground.
27. Zaheer Abbas (eight).
28. Queensland.

29. Frank Woolley of Kent.
30. Chris Tavaré.
31. Geoff Boycott.
32. Wilfred Rhodes, 4, 187.
33. Jim Laker.
34. Don Bradman and Bill Edrich.
35. Don Bradman in 1938, and Brian Lara in 1994.

36. 506–6 by South Australia v Queensland at Brisbane in 1991–92.
37. Ernest Tyldesley in 1927, and Don Bradman in 1947–48 and 1948 seasons.
38. Clarrie Grimmett, 513.
39. W V Raman of Tamil Nadu, 1,018 in 1988–89.
40. Geoff Boycott, 56.83 for a total of 48,426 runs in a career from 1962–1986.
41. John Maguire for Eastern Province, and formerly of Queensland and Australia, who took 76 in 1989–90.
42. Ken Barrington.

43. Orange Free State.
44. Geoff Hurst of Essex, in the 1996 Final when England beat Germany 4–2.
45. Zimbabwe, in October 1992 v India at Harare.
46. Everton Weekes, Clyde Walcott, and Frank Worrell, of the West Indies.
47. Sonny Ramadhin and Alf Valentine, the so-called 'spin bowlers and heroes of the Calypso'.
48. 1864.
49. Gundappa Vishwanath.

50. 715 by Brian Lara for Trinidad & Tobaco in 1993–94.
51. A E J Collins, 628 not out for Clark's House v North Town at Clifton College in 1899.
52. Matthew Hayden.
53. South Africa v India, First Test, Durban, 1992–93.
54. Graham Thorpe of Surrey.
55. Sheffield.
56. Carl Hooper for Kent v Durham.

57. Derbyshire v Lancashire and Middlesex.
58. Ashley Martyn.
59. Ernie McCormick v Worcestershire in 1938.
60. Mark Rushmere, 150 not out and 151 not out for a South African Invitation XI v England XI in 1989–90.
61. Graham Gooch, 1058 in 1990; Don Bradman, 1028 in 1934/1936–7, and 1005, 1936–7/1938; Gary Sobers, 1009 in 1957–58, 1958–59.
62. 1294 by Len Hutton in June 1949.
63. Herbert Sutcliffe (1924–25); Denis Compton (1947); Geoffrey Boycott (1971); Graham Gooch (1990–91.

Trivia 4

64. Walter Lawrence Trophy.
65. Kapil Dev for India v England at Lord's, 1990.
66. Graham Gooch, 333 and 123, England v India in 1990.
67. Dermot Reeve.
68. Brian Close v New Zealand in 1949, 18 years and 231 days.
69. Philip DeFreitas, when dismissing Blair Hartland in the second innings at Nottingham in 1994.
70. T A 'Andy' Lloyd of Warwickshire who was hit playing for England v West Indies in 1984.

71. 1971 – Ajit Wadekar.
72. 1603 for 28 wickets, England v India, 1990.
73. New Zealand 26 v England at Auckland in 1954–55.
74. Pakistan v Australia at Karachi, 1994–95.
75. Peter Loader for England v West Indies, Leeds, 1957.
76. Roland Butcher in West Indies in 1980–81.
77. Andrew Sandham, 325 v West Indies at Kingston, Jamaica, 1929–30, aged 40.

78. Ten, by Bob Taylor for England v India at Bombay in 1979–80.
79. Graham Gooch and Mike Atherton, 204 at Lord's and 225 at Old Trafford v India in 1990.
80. Trevor Franklin of New Zealand, 101 v England in 1990.
81. Jack MacBryan v South Africa in 1924.
82. David Houghton, 121 v India at Harare in 1992, in Zimbabwe's first Test match.
83. Wilfred Rhodes, 52 years 165 days, for England v West Indies at Kingston, 1929–30.
84. Desmond Haynes of West Indies, 88 out of 211 v Pakistan in Karachi, 1986–87; 75 out of 176 v England at The Oval, 1991; 143 out of 382 v Pakistan in Port of Spain, 1992–93.

Trivia 5

85. Wilf Slack.
86. Freddie Trueman.
87. David Gower.
88. Derek Underwood.
89. Hugh Tayfield – 170.
90. Denis Compton.
91. Geoffrey Boycott.

92. Robin Jackman.
93. Alec Stewart, 69 not out in a total of 175 by England v Pakistan at Lord's in 1992.
94. Jack Hobbs and Andrew Sandham.
95. Chris Old, who dismissed Wasim Raja, Wasim Bari, Iqbal Qasim, and Sikander Bakht.
96. 236 by Eric Rowan at Headingley in 1951.
97. Alan Melville of South Africa; 103 (Durban 1938–39), 189 and 104 not out (Trent Bridge), and 117 at Lord's in 1947.
98. Arthur Gilligan, 6–7; and Maurice Tate, 4–12.

99. George Lohmann.
100. Mudassar Nazar, 557 minutes for Pakistan v England at Lahore in 1977–78.
101. Graham Gooch and Mohammad Azharuddin at both Lord's and Old Trafford in 1990.
102. Ken Cranston for England at Leeds.
103. Tom Goddard at Johannesburg, 1938–39.
104. C Aubrey Smith.
105. Cliff Gladwin.

Trivia 6

106. Surrey by Essex at Chelmsford.
107. Melbourne Cricket Ground in 1877, Australia v England.
108. Chris Lewis and Phil DeFreitas.
109. D V 'Syd' Lawrence.
110. 46 at Port of Spain, Trinidad, 1993–94.
111. Wayne Larkins of Northants, now Durham, in 1993.
112. Gordon Greenidge.

113. 332–7 v Australia in Melbourne in 1928–29.
114. Wally Hammond, Colin Cowdrey, Ian Botham, and Graham Gooch.
115. Wally Hammond for Gloucestershire v Surrey at Cheltenham in 1928.
116. Len Hutton, England v South Africa at The Oval in 1951.
117. John Carr of Middlesex.
118. Jack Hobbs, aged 41; 211 for England v South Africa at Lord's in 1924.
119. K D Walters (Australia, 1968–69); G. S. Chappell (Australia, 1975–76); and S. M. Gavaskar (India, 1970–71 and 1978–79).

120. Les Ames, 123 for England v South Africa, The Oval, 1935.
121. H. Wood, 134 not out for England v South Africa at Cape Town in 1891–92.
122. Eric Rowan, aged 42; 236 South Africa v England at Headingley in 1951.
123. David Hookes, 107 for South Australia v Victoria at Adelaide in 1982–83.
124. 4–362 by Arthur Mailey of NSW v Victoria in 1926–27.
125. J C 'Farmer' White of Somerset.
126. New Zealand v England at Christchurch in 1991–92. (Robin Smith 96, Allan Lamb 93, Dipak Patel 99, and John Wright 99.)